Mark Duginske
Karl Eichhorn

**Precision Machinery Techniques—
A Woodworker's Handbook**

Precision Machinery Techniques
A Woodworker's Handbook

With useful tips and jigs for everyone

Mark Duginske, Karl Eichhorn

Edited by INCA Ltd, Teufenthal/Switzerland

1 st English edition September 1984

Copyrights 1984 INCA Maschinen und Apparate AG,
CH-5723 Teufenthal/Switzerland

ISBN 0-8069-6328-X

Precision Machinery Techniques—
A Woodworker's Handbook

Table of Contents

FOREWORD

FOREWORD

Precision Machinery Techniques—A Woodworker's Handbook was written in collaboration with The INCA Machine Manufacturing Company of Teufenthal, Switzerland. INCA is a leading manufacturer of woodworking machinery for the hobbyist and professional shop. It's products are distributed throughout the world.

Although the drawings used throughout this book are of INCA Brand Machinery, all of the techniques and jigs described are general in nature and can be used on all properly maintained woodworking machinery.

Working with the Table Saw

Cutting tools, working methods, auxiliary equipment

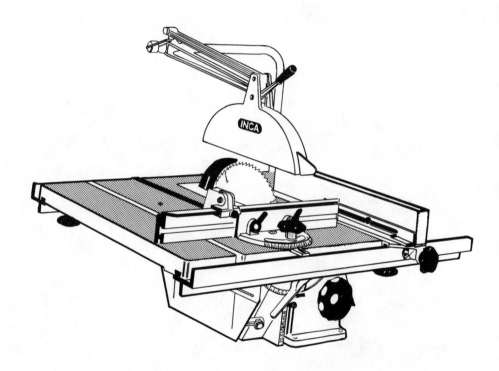

Saw Blades

Circular Saw Blades

One of the most important parts of the table saw is the blade itself, a flat steel disc with sharp teeth around the outer edge. The shape and sharpness of these teeth, the speed of the blade and the speed at which a board is fed through the saw all affect the quality of the cut.

Each tooth on a 10" diameter sawblade will strike the wood at a speed of about 112 miles per hour! Because of the high speeds involved, you can imagine how critical it is for the blades to be in top condition at all times. All the teeth must be sharp and ground at the same height so they describe a perfect circle as the blade rotates. Never use a blade that has cracks in its teeth or body. Regularly take your blades to a professional sharpening shop for inspection and regrinding.

The pattern of the teeth and the angles at which the teeth are ground vary according to the type of material to be cut and the blade and feed speeds. Some general tooth patterns are described below, but for a specific application, consult your local dealer who will recommend the best blade.

The speed at which you feed your work into the blade depends on: the hardness of the material being cut; the thickness; the number of teeth on the blade; their configuration; and the speed of the blade.

Too fast a feed speed will give a poor cut and can make the saw labor unnecessarily. Too slow can cause burning. You should feed your work at a smooth, even rate. Try not to stop feeding in the middle of a cut. The scraping of the teeth against the work can cause a lot of heat which may draw the temper from the teeth or scorch the wood.

Blades with Set Teeth

Steel saw blades' bodies and teeth are formed from the same steel plate, usually a chrome nickel steel alloy that holds up well in use. The teeth are alternately set to the left and right. The blade makes a cut that is slightly wider than the blade plate so that it can pass through the cut without jamming or burning.

Blades intended to rip, or cut along the long grain of a board, have few teeth and the individual teeth are ground straight across like tiny chisels.

Blades intended for crosscutting have a larger number of teeth each of which is filed at a slight angle. Mitring and plywood or veneer cutting blades are special blades that have the largest number of teeth and cut smoothest.

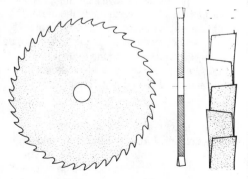

Combination Blades

Another type of blade is the "combination" type. This blade often has its teeth arranged in groups. In one example, a blade may have groups of five teeth. The first four are ground and set like a crosscut blade and the fifth tooth is ground straight across like a rip tooth. This blade works well for a variety of different cuts.

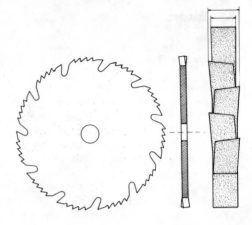

Hollow Ground Blades

Another class of blades is the hollow ground type. The teeth on this kind of blade have no set at all. Instead, the body of the blade is ground thinner toward the center. This relief grinding allows the body of the blade to pass through the saw cut. Hollow ground blades are among the smoothest cutting blades. If you use them, be sure that your sharpening service recognizes that they are hollow ground – not to be set!

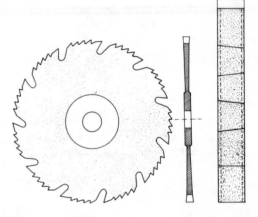

Carbide Tipped Blades

Carbide tipped blades have a flat steel body and small tips of carbide brazed onto the teeth. The teeth of a carbide blade are not set, but are slightly wider that the width of the body. Carbide is a very hard material and the teeth will stay sharp a long time. But be careful, carbide is also brittle and can chip or crack if mishandled.

There are a very large variety of carbide blades available for cutting almost any material. Some of these blades will cut fast and rough and others will leave a glass smooth finish. Consult your dealer for advice in selecting carbide blades.

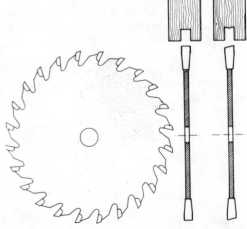

The Rip Fence

To make any cut along the length of a board, parallel to the grain, (ripping) you will use the rip fence. This is a straight, parallel-sided bar which clamps to the front rail of the table saw. A longer fence is available as an option, which also has a clamp on the back rail. There are holes bored through each rip fence so that you can use screws or bolts to attach wooden auxiliary fences that are higher or longer than the standard fence. Make sure that their faces are planed flat and parallel before you attach them.

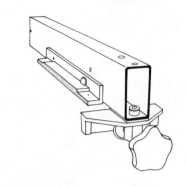

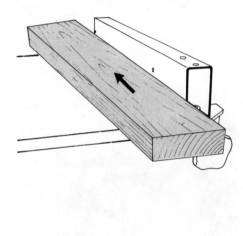

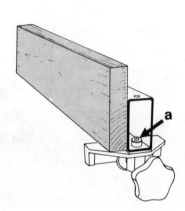

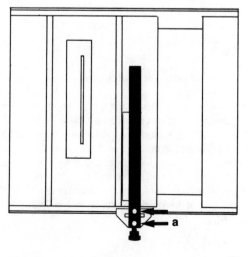

It is very important that the rip fence be exactly in line (parallel) with the mitre guide slots in the saw table. To check this, place the fence, with the sliding auxiliary fence installed, exactly next to a mitre guide slot. Place your finger in the slot and feel along the edge of the fence. If the fence is not perfectly aligned, loosen the two socket head screws (marked "a") and realign the fence. Then retighten the socket head screws.

The rip fence can be positioned either left or right of the blade, and the auxiliary fence can be positioned on either the left or right side of the fence.

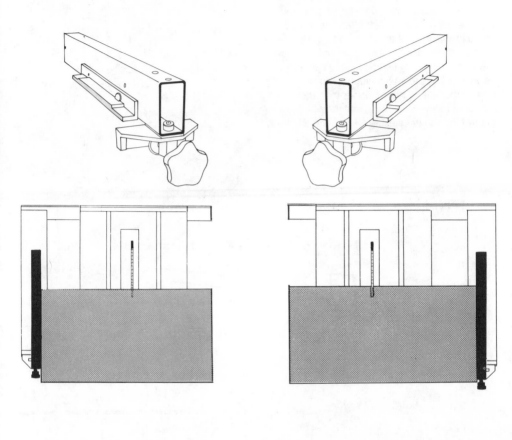

The Rip Fence Micro-Adjuster

The rip fence micro-adjuster is an optional accessory that can be attached to the fence. The adjuster is threaded into the fence clamp casting and clamped to the rail beside the fence. The fence clamp is then loosened slightly and adjusted by rotating the knurled metal wheel of the micro adjuster. Each graduation mark on the left side of the knurled metal wheel equals 0.004".

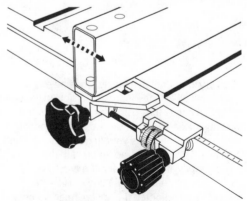

A Jig to Cut Corner Glue Blocks

Corner blocks are often glued behind mitred corners as a reinforcement. This jig, consisting of two beveled sides and a front block joining them into a "v" groove will help you easily cut square sticks into triangular strips.

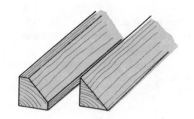

How this jig can be used with the safety holddown is described later.

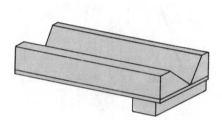

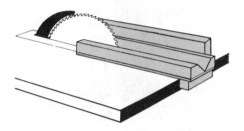

Setting Blade Height

The blade should be set so that, for normal cutting, the deepest gullet between the teeth is level with the top of the board, but never with the tip of the teeth more than ½ " above the top of the board.

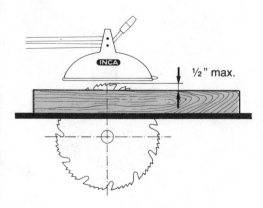

½" max.

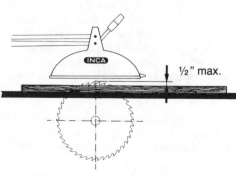

½" max.

Preventing Kickback

When a board is ripped along the grain it sometimes may open or close around the saw blade. In the first case it may jam between the fence and the blade and cause burning or kickback. In the second case it may squeeze the blade and, again, cause burning or kickback.

Either case can be prevented by the correct use of the splitter and the auxiliary fence.

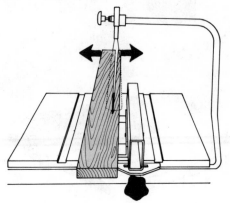 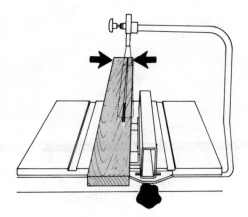

The Auxiliary Fence

Each fence comes with an auxiliary fence that is held to the main fence by a screw and knurled nut for easy adjustment. This special fence leaves a space between the main fence and the board after the board is cut so that it will not be burnt or kicked back by the rising teeth of the saw blade if the board opens as it is cut.

The auxiliary fence is also useful for cutting veneers and thin stock because it rests flat on the table and will not let thin stock slide under the fence.

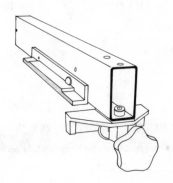

Correct Positioning of the
Auxiliary Fence

The far end of the fence should be about 1" past
the point where the teeth of the saw blade begin
to enter the top of the wood being cut. This
distance is marked "e" in the illustration.

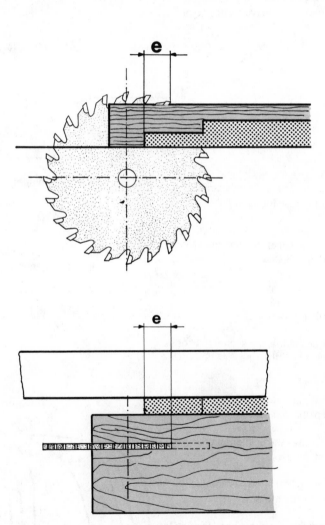

The Splitter (Riving Knife)

The splitter prevents the two sides of the saw cut from closing against the sides of the blade during ripping. If you do not use the splitter when ripping, the board may kick back at you.

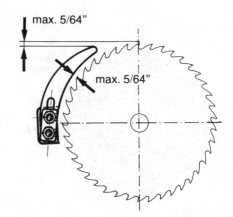

Also, the splitter keeps the board running true to the blade and fence as it is being cut. This will help make a cleaner cut during ripping. For the best results, the splitter must be the correct thickness and curve for the type and size of blade used. A variety of splitters are available for various blades.

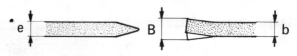

The splitter should be slightly thinner than the width of the saw cut. The splitter thickness can be calculated with these formulae:

For standard, all steel blades, the splitter thickness should be half of the combined width of the saw cut and the thickness of the blade body:

B = Width of saw cut.
b = Thickness of the blade body
e = Thickness of the splitter

For carbide tipped blades, the splitter thickness should be 0.008" LESS than the thickness of the saw cut:

B = Width of saw cut.
e = Thickness of the splitter.

Standard blade:

$$e = \frac{B + b}{2}$$

Carbide tipped blade:
$$e = B - 0.008"$$

Remember to remove the splitter for grooving, moulding, or set-in cuts.

The long, narrow splitter shown is used for large blades, 7" to 10" in diameter.

The short, wide splitter shown is used for smaller blades, 5" to 7" in diameter.

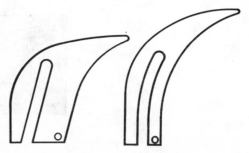

Correct and Incorrect splitter settings

The splitter is set too low. A board that touches the rising teeth could be kicked back at you.

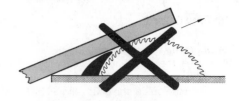

Set correctly, the splitter will keep the board from touching the back of the blade.

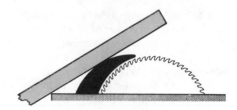

This splitter is too far away from the blade. Wood chips, or worse, fingers (!), could be caught between the blade and the splitter, causing an accident.

With the splitter as close to the blade as possible, nothing could be caught between them.

If it is too high, the splitter will prevent shallow cuts or grooves.

The top of the splitter should be about 1/32" below the top of the blade. This will allow the shallowest cuts possible.

Correct use of the splitter, the auxiliary fence and the safety guard over the blade will prevent accidents and make your woodworking safer and more enjoyable.

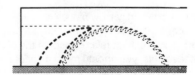

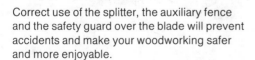

The Saw Guard

The saw guard was developed to safely cover the blade and to be easy to reposition for a variety of operations. After setting the fence, or mitre guide, the guard should be lowered nearly to the top of the board being cut. The space between the top of the board and the bottom of the guard should be no more than half of the thickness of your index finger.

Many of the illustrations here show the guard removed or raised. This is only for clarity.

You should always use the guard when using the table saw.

When ripping with the fence to the right of the saw blade, use your left hand to press the board against the fence in front of the blade. Your right hand is used to push the board into the saw blade. Use a push stick for any small pieces you are cutting, and it's a good idea to curl your fingers under your hand (like making a fist) and push with your palm.

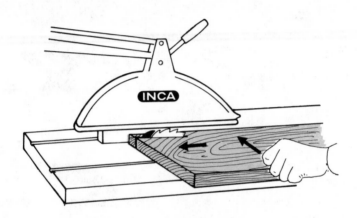

Using Push Sticks

Cutting small and narrow pieces is more dangerous than cutting larger ones because your hands and fingers are closer to the blade. For these cuts, you should make a variety of push sticks out of scrap wood as shown.

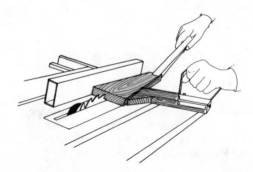

A push stick handle is a worthwhile addition to the workshop. It has five steel points to hold scrap wood blocks used for pushing or maneuvering wood pieces around all kinds of woodworking machinery.

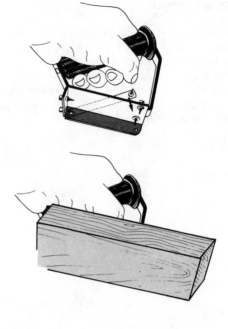

A homemade push stick

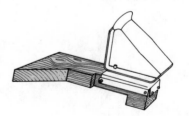

This wedge shaped piece, used with a handle, is very useful for pressing wood against the fence and for removing small cutoff pieces. If any cutoff pieces come to rest near the blade, shut off the machine before brushing them away.

Sawing Long Boards

To rip very long boards, you should either have
someone to help you or an outfeed roller (as
shown below) to support the weight of the board.
If neither is available, make the cut in two
operations. First, cut to the center of the board.
Second, reverse the board and complete the cut
from the opposite direction. Be sure to turn the
board over in order to hold the same edge
against the fence for both cuts.

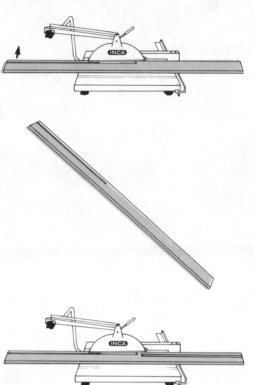

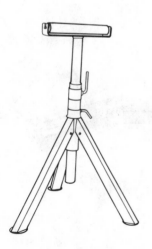

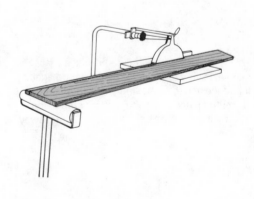

Squaring the Edge of a Rough Board

The edge of board to be ripped must be straight to get a smooth, straight cut. If a jointer is not available to properly prepare a rough board, the edge can be sawn straight if the board is held on a special jig. This jig is a flat board with a strip glued or screwed to the bottom that slides in the mitre quide slot. A crosspiece at the end prevents the work from sliding as it is cut. Place the board on the jig. And slide the whole assembly in the mitre guide slot. When one edge of the board has been out straight and square, you can hold that side against the regular fence and make your next cut in the usual way.

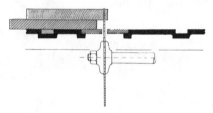

The Safety Hold-down

The safety hold-down was originally designed for use with the moulding head. It is, however, very useful for a number of other common cuts. The hold-down is held to the table by a bolt and features a bottom foot that presses down against the table and a side foot that presses in against the fence.

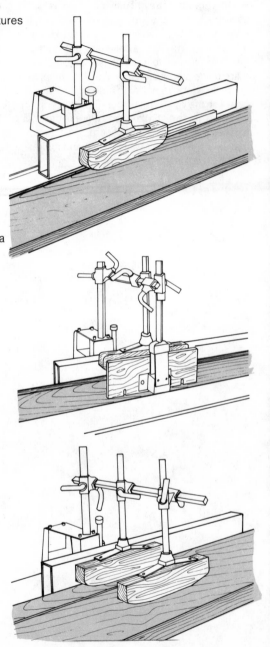

Ripping Narrow Strips

Here, only the bottom foot is used to help guide a wide board as you cut narrow strips.

Grooving the Edge of a Small Board

The bottom and side feet are used to hold this small board firmly against the fence and table.

Ripping a Wide, Long Board

Two bottom feet are used, one on each side of the cut, to hold down a large board for ripping.

Grooving the Edge of a Wide Panel

To support the panel a high wooden face should be bolted to the side of the rip fence. The safety-hold-down is mounted on the left side of the table and only the side pressure foot is used, as, shown.

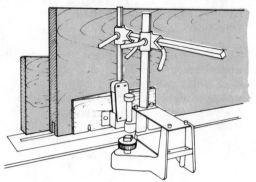

Sawing with a Pattern

Using a pattern is the best way to duplicate a number of identical pieces when the sides are straight, but at odd angles to each other. First, make a pattern that is exactly the size and shape you need. Then, mount a wooden guide fence on the side of the main fence. This guide fence must be high enough to allow the cutoff to pass under it, and its left edge must be exactly in line with the left edge of the saw blade.

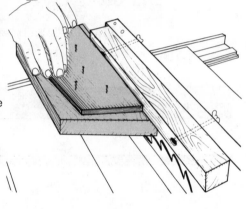

The pattern is mounted to the board to be cut by tacks, screws, or double sided tape. As the edge of the pattern is pushed along the guide fence, the board below is cut to exactly the size required.

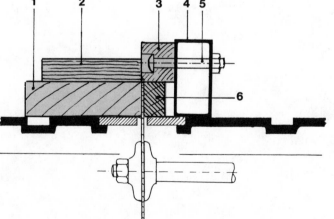

1. The board being cut
2. The pattern
3. The guide fence
4. The main fence
5. Bolts to hold guide fence in place
6. Cut off waste

Cutting Tapers and Wedges
One-sided tapers

If you are only going to cut a taper on one side of a board, a step jig will do the job very well. The stock is held against the step, and the jig and workpiece are pushed through the saw together. Here, a handle is mounted to the jig for safety and easy handling. The width of the step ("a") is equal to the rise. The height of the step ("b") should be as small as possible for the best accuracy.

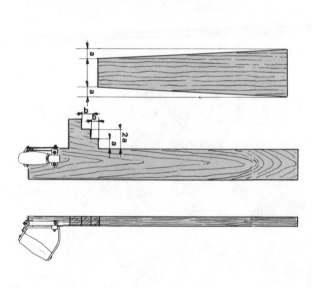

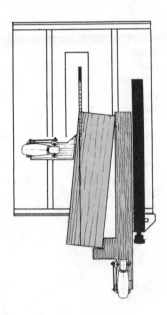

Double-sided tapers

Often tapers are cut on both sides of a board
The jig used is similiar to the previous one,
except it has two steps. Use the upper step for
the first cut, flip the board over, 180 degrees, and
hold the fresh cut side at the lower step for the
second cut.

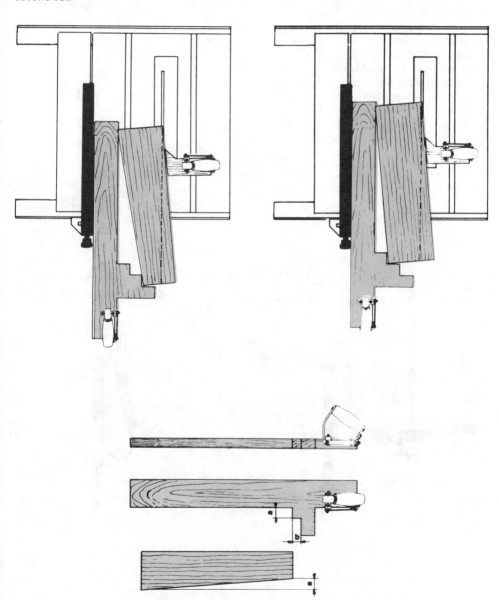

The Adjustable Taper Jig

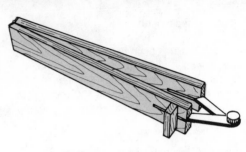

A hinged jig can be adjusted to various tapers or angles and can be very useful in making tapered chair or furniture legs. This kind of jig can be made in your shop, or can be purchased from your tool dealer.

Setting the angle of the jig

If you know the angle of the taper, you can use the protractor of the mitre guide and a square to transfer that angle to the jig. Alternately, you can place the mitre guide upside down, with its head hanging over the back of the table and the face pressed against the rear table rails. Use the mitre guide bar itself to set the angle of the taper jig.

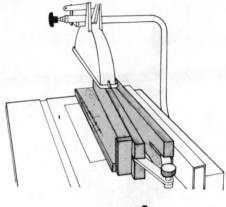

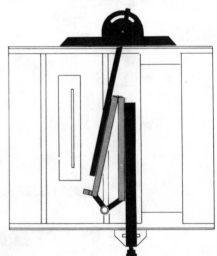

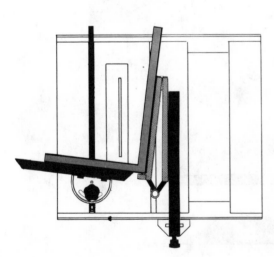

If you do not know the angle, the distance ("d") between the ends of the jig can be calculated with this formula:

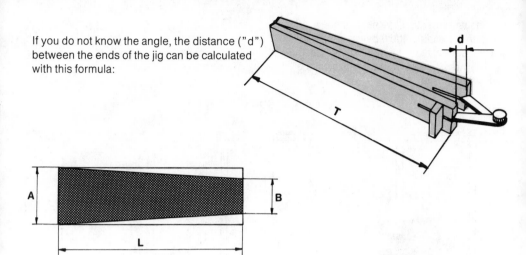

$$d = \frac{A-B}{2 \times L} \times T$$

d = The distance between the ends of the taper jig
T = The length of the taper jig
A = The widest measurement of the completed taper
B = The narrowest measurement of the completed taper
L = The overall length of the completed taper

This measurement "d" is the distance between the ends of the taper jig. This will give the correct taper for one side. To get the taper of the other side, double this distance for the second cut.

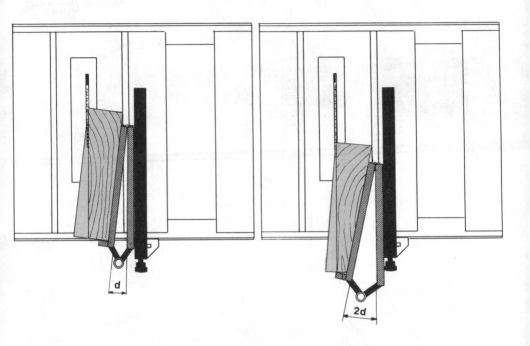

Cutting a four sided taper for a chair leg

1. Cut a taper along one side
2. Cut the same taper along an adjoining side
3. Double the angle of the taper jig, and make the third cut
4. Cut the fourth side at the same setting as the third.

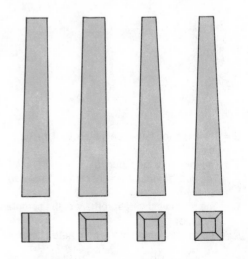

Cutting Wedges

You can easily make a series of wedges using a jig made from a piece of scrap wood. The jig should slide along the rip fence as you hold the work in the notch. Flip the work over after each cut to make the next wedge. The jig shown uses a handle to push it with. When you cut the wedges, have the grain of the wood run along the length of the wedge. This will make the wedge stronger.

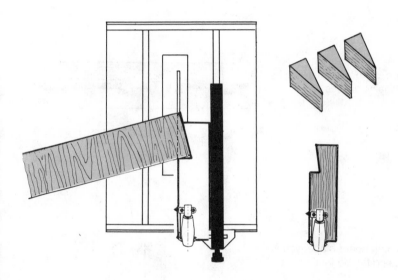

Rabbeting and Grooving

Rabbets, grooves and dados are shallow cuts that are wider than a standard saw blade. A rabbet (or shoulder) is a step in the edge of a board. A groove runs along the length of a board, parallel to the grain. A dado is a groove which runs across the grain.

These cuts can be made with: a grooving blade; a dado set; a straight end moulding cutter; a standard blade which is tilted by wobble washers; or by a standard blade in several passes.

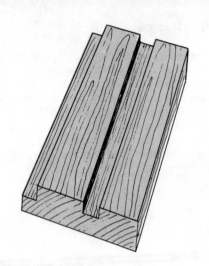

Using a standard blade, a groove can be cut by making several overlapping passes.

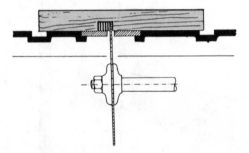

To cut a rabbet with a standard blade, you will make two passes, using the rip fence as a guide and support.

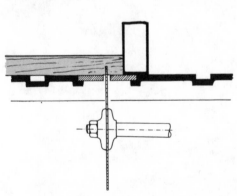

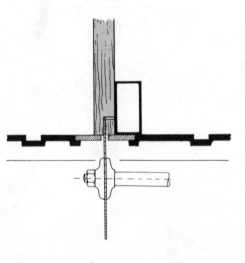

Wobble Washers

Wobble washers are two large wedge shaped washers. To install these, remove the blade, put the wobble washers on the arbor and replace the blade, the outside stabilizing washers and arbor nut. Both washers go inside the blade as shown below.

Rotating the wobble washers in opposite directions tilts the saw blade slightly. As it rotates, the edge of the blade will move left to right and make a wider cut than it normally would. The maximum width of the groove that can be cut varies according to the diameter of the blade used. For example, a 10" blade can be made to cut about a 5/8" groove using wobble washers. You should select a blade which is appropriate for the cutting you will do. A crosscut blade for dados, a rip blade for grooves.

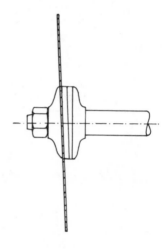

The adjustment of the width will take a couple of trial cuts on scrap wood. Remember to tighten the arbor nut before turning on the saw.

Cutting a groove with the wobble washers. Use the mitre guide for crosscut dados and the rip fence for grooves.

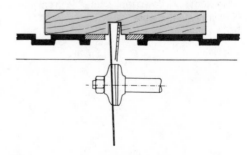

When you cut rabbets, you should use the mitre guide or the ripfence with the wooden auxiliary fence for moulding (described later).

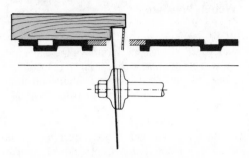

Keep in mind that the bottom of the groove cut by the wobble washer and blade combination will be slightly curved, as the blade scribes the arc of a circle as it rotates.

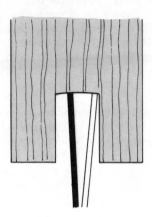

Using the Moulding Head

With a straight cutter mounted in the moulding head you can make grooves or rabbets. Here the bottom hold down foot is used to press the work firmly to the table.

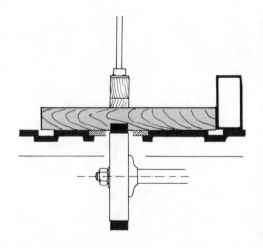

The Rabbet Milling Fence

The auxiliary wooden fence is bolted to the rip fence to mill a rabbet. This special fence has a curved cut out around the blade or cutterhead. The safety hold-down should also be used, of course.

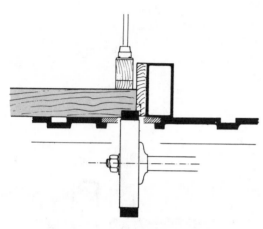

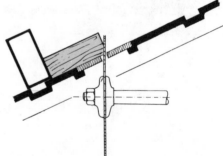

Chamfers and Bevels

Using the Saw Blade

Chamfers are angled cuts along the edge of a board. To make these cuts, the saw table must be tilted. The rip fence should be positioned to the left of the blade (the downhill side). This way, you have gravity working in your favor to support the work and hold it firmly against the table and fence. The splitter will keep the cut off strips from sliding against the blade.

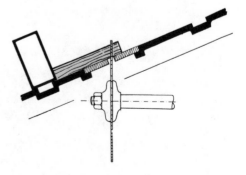

Using the Moulding Head with 45 Degree Cutters

By cutting bevels this way, you will not have to tilt the table, which is a particular advantage when working with large boards. The auxiliary wooden moulding fence should be used and, of course, the safety holdown. Bevel the front edge first to prevent tearing out of wood chips.

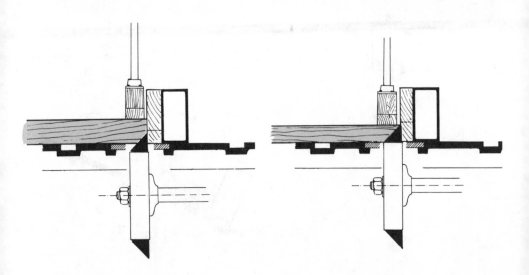

Panel Raising

Raised panels make very attractive doors and are quite easy to make. The first cut is the shallow one, at the bottom of the shoulder. The cheeks of the panel are then cut by tilting the table and holding the panel against a tall wooden fence attached to the rip fence. The safety holdown should be used, as shown, to help make a smoother cut.

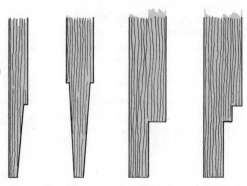

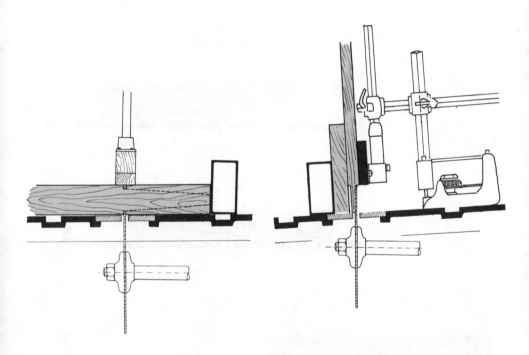

Set-in Work

Sometimes you will want to begin or end a cut somewhere before the end of the board. This is called set-in work. To do this safely, you will need to make a special anti-kickback fence, which is bolted to the rip fence.

For a cut that starts in the center of a board and runs off the end, the anti-kickback fence will have a stop only in front of the blade.
The splitter must be removed for this operation.

Hold the end of the board against the stop and lower il onto the blade. When it is flat against the table, continue the cut as in a normal rip cut. Keep all fingers clear and use the guard and appropriate push sticks.

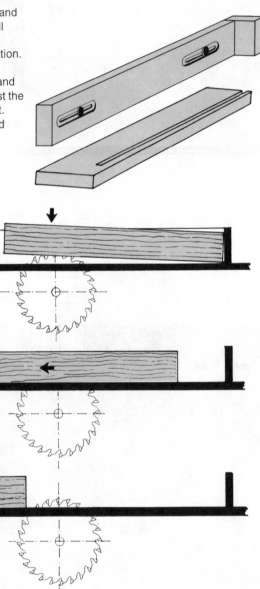

For a cut that starts and stops within the board, a
fence with two stops is necessary. Start as
before, and after you reach the second stop, lift
the board straight up and clear of the blade.
Keep fingers away from the blade!

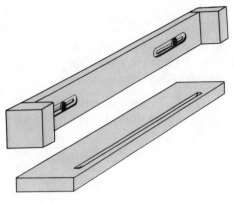

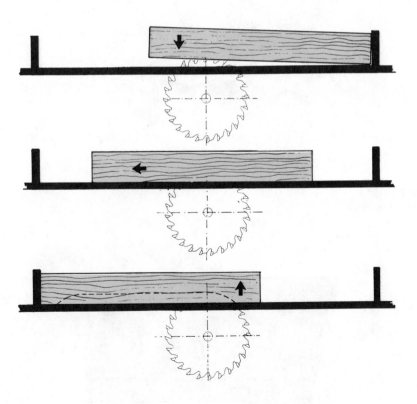

The Mitre Guide

Cross and mitre cuts are made using by the mitre guide to push and support the work. The mitre guide has a protractor head calibrated from 90 to 45 degrees in both directions. This head is attached to a bar which slides in the grooves in the saw table.

The face of the protractor supports the board while cutting and can slide left or right, so that the end is positioned as close to the saw blade as possible.

The drop stop is attached to the mitre guide face for cutting off several pieces to the same length. Mitre guide faces "a" and sliding bars "b" are available in several lengths.

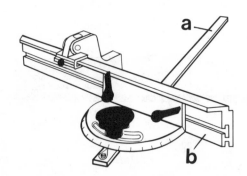

These cuts are made with the mitre guide:

1. Crosscut
2. Beveled crosscut
3. Mitre cut
4. Compound mitre cut

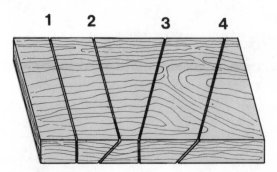

There are two ways to set the mitre guide accurately at 90 degrees. The first is to use a good square between the bar and the face.

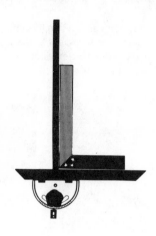

The second method is to flip the mitre guide over and place the protractor head over the front of the saw, hanging upside down. Loosen the locking knob and press the face against the front of the saw. Then tighten the locking knob.

You can check your setting by cutting a flat,
thickness planed board in half. Reverse one side
and place the ends together. If there is any error,
it will be doubled and easy to see.

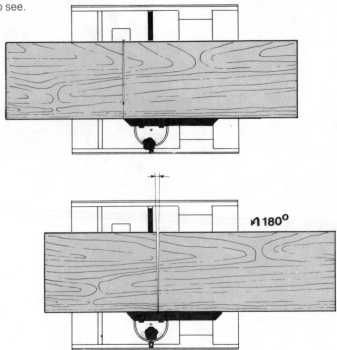

The Straight Crosscut

With the protractor head and the saw table set at
90 degrees, slide the mitre guide and the work
through the rotating blade.

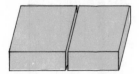

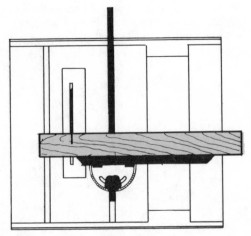

Here, the mitre guide bar has been placed in the
right hand mitre groove of the saw table. Many
woodworkers prefer to use the left hand groove
for most cuts. This is strictly a matter of
convenience and personal preference.

The Drop Stop

The drop stop, which can be mounted anywhere along the mitre guide face, is very useful for cutting several pieces to the same length and will help prevent the board from shifting as it is cut. Additional mitre guide faces up to 39" long are available, and when used with two or more drop stops can make your work faster and easier.

To use two drop stops, follow this procedure: first use the outer stop to cut one end of the board square; second, place the end just cut square against the inner stop and cut it off. Many pieces can be cut off to the same length extremely accurately by this method.

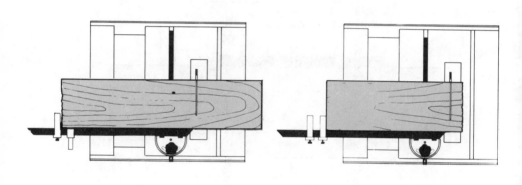

The Auxiliary Fence as a Cutoff Stop

For cutting off several small pieces to the same length, you can use the auxiliary fence attached to the main fence. This will provide a space for the small pieces between the main fence and the blade without jamming and kicking back.

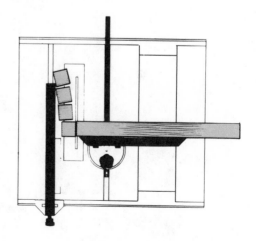

Cutting Large Panels

To cut large panel, it is a good idea to increase the size of your saw table. You can do this by mounting auxiliary tables (1) to the left and right of the saw on longer rails (2) available up to 59" long.

The mitre guide will be mounted in reverse to its normal prosition and the work held in place with a bar clamp, as shown, to hold it as it is cut.

You will find that it may be useful to use a longer table bar (3) and longer mitre face (4) for working with large boards.

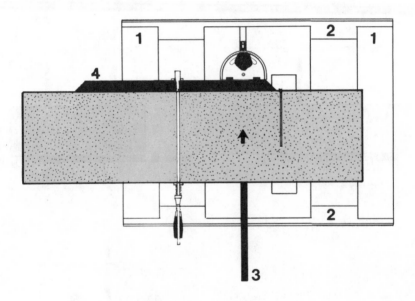

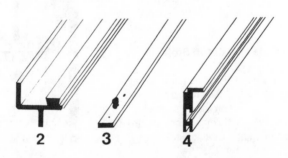

An extension table support leg is a worthwhile accessory, especially if you are going to do a lot of work with the tables extended far from the saw. They increase stability and can be adjusted in length for use on uneven floors or when the table is tilted.

A sliding table, which runs on roller bearings and steel tracks, is also available. This is particularly useful if you have to cut a lot of panels. But, to be most effective, it should be positioned as close to the edge of the main saw table as possible.

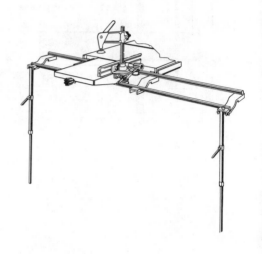

Making Parallel Grooves

When you have to make a series of parallel grooves, all evenly spaced, there are two methods that work well.

The first method is to use the Finger Joint attachment installed on the mitre guide in place of the normal fence. The distance, between the metal pin on this attachment and the side of the blade determines the space between the grooves.

Make the first cut with the end of the board against the pin. For the second cut, lift the board and place the groove just cut over the metal pin. Continue in this way until all the grooves are cut.
Another method is to use the rip fence and a series of blocks. The first block is clamped to the saw table. The others are placed between the first and the fence, which is firmly pressed

against the last block. Make the first cut, remove one block and slide the fence to its new position. This method works well on very wide pieces or when ripping grooves along the length of a board.

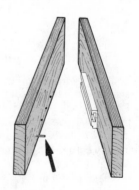

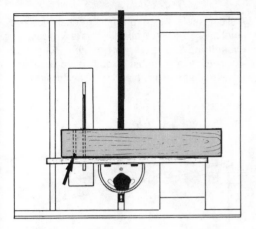
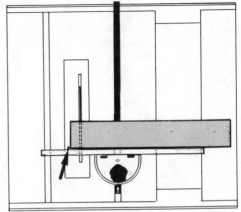

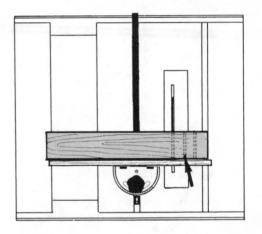

The width of each distance piece (x) equals the space between grooves plus the width of one groove. They are placed on the right side of the circular saw blade and are held in place with a clamp. A distance piece is to be removed after every cut and the rip fence adjusted accordingly to the right.
This method is well suited for pieces with wide long grooves.

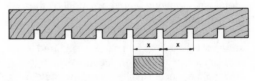

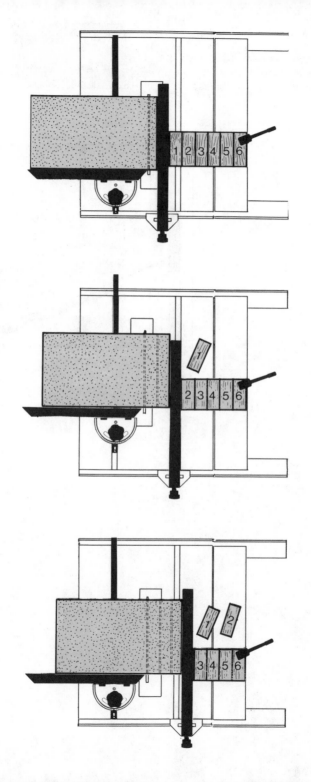

Straight Mitres

For a straight mitre, the table is level and only the mitre protractor is angled. Again, the use of the drop stop is recommended, or you can use the fence as shown.

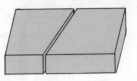

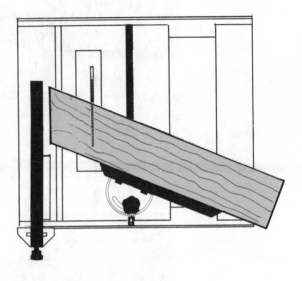

The Mitred Frame

Mitred frames require eight cuts, one on each end of each board. These cuts must be very accurate, both in the angle and in the length, for the frame to come out square with tight fitting, attractive corner joints.

When you are working with stock that is square or rectangular in cross section, you can make all the cuts with the mitre guide at one angle, as illustrated below. This position will help you work accurately because the moving blade will have the tendency to slide the work down the mitre guide, tightly against the stop. This is the prefered position. For wider work, however, you may find it easier to angle the mitre guide in the opposite direction. This will leave more room in front of the blade-

Before making the cuts for your finished pieces, make a test cut on a piece of scrap and check the angle. A mitre square can be used or, better, make two cuts, place them together and check with a good try square. The advantage of this is that the error will be doubled and easy to see.

Tear-out can be avoided during mitre cuts by placing a thickness-planed piece of scrap behind the board you are cutting. Cut through both at the same time.

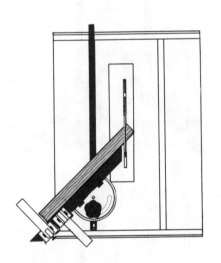

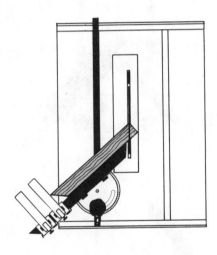

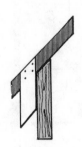

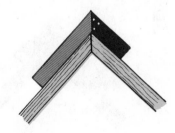

If you are going to do a lot of framing, or if you will be working with moulded frame stock, using two mitre guides is an excellent idea. For production work, it is nearly essential.

The first mitre guide is placed in the right mitre slot and adjusted for 45 degrees as previously described. Make a test cut, of course, to check accuracy. Then, place the other mitre guide in the left slot and set it from the first, using a good square which extends from one mitre face to the other.

Now your two mitre guides are set with a 90 angle between their faces. You can use them to cut all types and shapes of moulding.

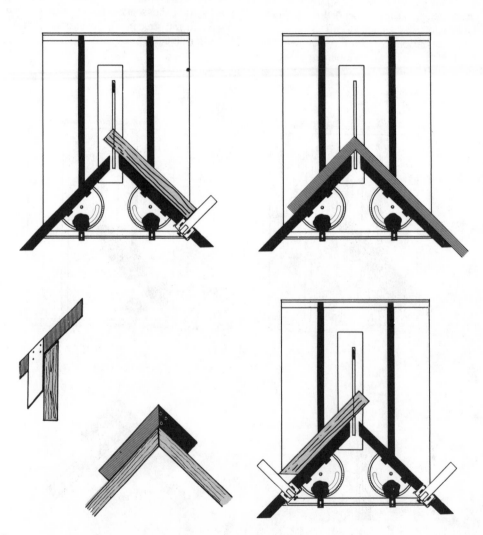

Sometimes reversing the mitre guides will make it easier to handle large or odd shaped pieces. In these cases is is not neccessary to change the angle. Just move the right mitre guide to the left slot and the left to the right slot. The angle between the two will always remain at the original setting of 90 degrees.

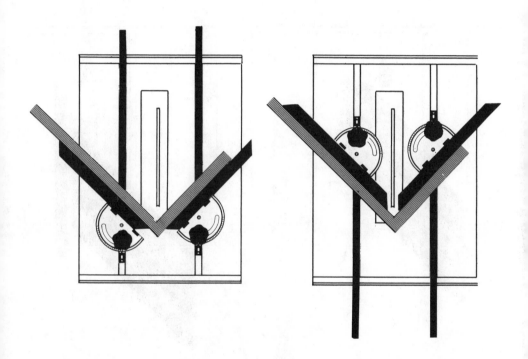

The Herringbone Pattern

The herringbone pattern makes a very attractive panel or cutting board. To make this, glue up a panel made of strips of various types of woods. Stagger the ends as shown.

Place this board, when the glue has dried, against a mitre guide, set at 45 degrees, that has been reversed in its slot. Hold the board to the mitre guide with a clamp for safety. Cut off the end.

The rest of the cuts will be made using the rip fence and sliding auxiliary fence as shown.

Finally, reverse every other piece and glue together inside a frame.

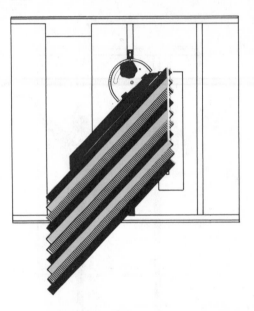

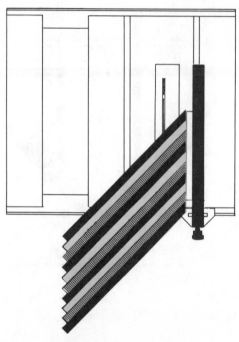

The Compound Mitre

A compound mitre is made by tilting the table
and changing the angle of the mitre guide. Use
the drop stop if possible, to keep the board firm
and stable while cutting.

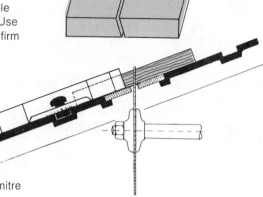

The Compound Mitre Box

A compound angle cut is a variation of the mitre
cut. To produce a 4, 6, or 8. sided funnel or
tapered box, both the table and the mitre guide
head must be set at different angles. For very
large pieces, use the adjustable taper jig instead
of the mitre guide.

This table shows the correct setting of the table
and mitre guide angles:

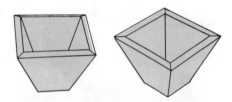

Slope	4 Sided Box		6 Sided Box		8 Sided Box	
	Table Angle	Mitre Guide	Table Angle	Mitre Guide	Table Angle	Mitre Guide
5°	44 3/4°	85°	29 3/4°	87 1/2°	22 1/4°	88°
10°	44 1/4°	80 1/4°	29 1/2°	84 1/2°	22°	86°
15°	43 1/4°	75 1/2°	29°	81 3/4°	21 1/2°	84°
20°	41 3/4°	71 1/4°	28 1/4°	79°	21°	82°
25°	40°	67°	27 1/4°	76 1/2°	20 1/4°	80°
30°	37 3/4°	63 1/2°	26°	74°	19 1/2°	78 1/4°
35°	35 1/2°	60 1/4°	24 1/2°	71 3/4°	18 1/4°	76 3/4°
40°	32 1/2°	57 1/4°	22 3/4°	69 3/4°	17°	75°
45°	30°	54 3/4°	21°	67 3/4°	15 3/4°	73 3/4°
50°	27°	52 1/2°	19°	66 1/4°	14 1/4°	72 1/2°
55°	24°	50 3/4°	16 3/4°	64 3/4°	12 1/2°	71 1/4°
60°	21°	49°	14 1/2°	63 1/2°	11°	70 1/4°

For example:
If you want to cut a box with the sides inclined 20
degrees, then you will set the table at 41-3/4
degrees and the mitre guide at 71-1/4 degrees

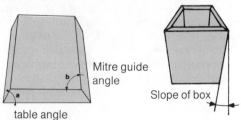

table angle

Mitre guide
angle

Slope of box

Set the mitre guide and table at the correct angle.

Place the mitre guide in the right hand table groove. Use the rip fence with the auxiliary fence as a cutoff guide. Clamp the board to the mitre guide before cutting to prevent it from sliding as the cut is made.

After the the first cut, turn the board over to make the second cut, and over again to make the third and finally the fourth. Using the same board to make all sides will, in the long run, be easier and more accurate.

Finally, the ends of the pieces have to be cut off with the table tilted at 20 degrees so that the completed pieces will stand flat on its end.

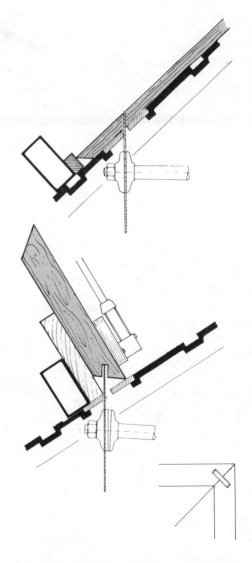

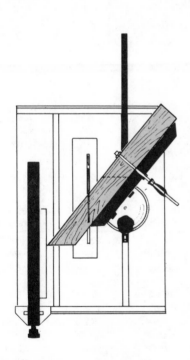

A spline and groove joint is a strong, attractive joint for this type of construction. For the example above, leave the table tilted at 41-3/4 degrees, and hold the board, on edge, against the fence to make the groove. The spline should be made of a thin strip of solid wood or plywood, with its grain running in the same direction as the boards it joins.

Tenons and Notches

Tenons are one of the most common joints found in woodworking, especially in furniture work. Not only are they structurally strong, but they can be a very attractive joints and easy to make with the right jig.

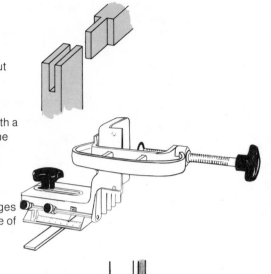

The Tenoning Jig holds the work vertically with a clamp. A bar, mounted in its base, slides in the mitre guide slot of the table saw. Two stops control the left-to-right position of the board.

To use this device, put the board in place as shown. To prevent tear out as the blade emerges from the back of the workpiece, install a piece of scrap with two screws (arrows). Slide the jig, with the board clamped in place, through the blade and back again to make the cut.

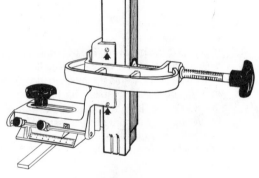

Four Ways to Cut Tenons

1. With a standard blade and wobble washers. The only disadvantage with this method is the slight curvature at the top of the cut.

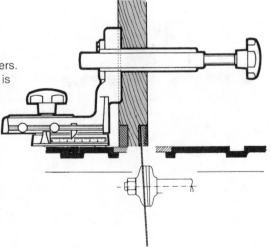

2. With a series of cuts.
   The cut must usually be sanded after making
   several passes.

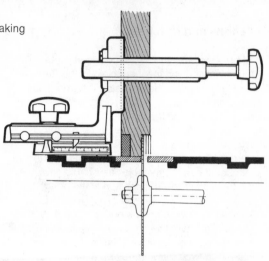

3. With four saw cuts
   This may be the best way. First use the fence
   as a stop and cut the shoulders using the
   mitre guide. Then clamp the piece in the
   tenon jig and cut the cheeks. This has the
   advantage of avoiding a blade change, and
   of severing the wood fibers by the shoulder
   cut thereby completely eliminating
   tearout when cutting the cheek.

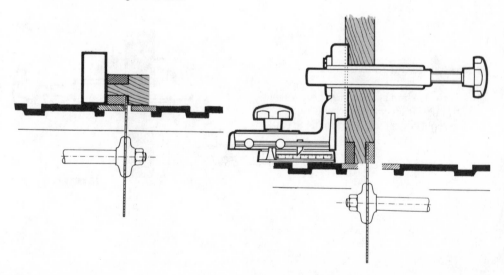

4. Using a dado or grooving blade.
   This method can complete the job in only two cuts, but you must use a back up piece to avoid tearout.

Setting The Tenoning Jig

Tenons are usually made to be fitted into mortises that have been made by a mortising attachment or another machine. The easiest way to set the tenon device is to use a mortise as a guide.

First, make a sample mortise which is open on one end, or cut through a mortise that has already been made. Place this piece in the tenon device as shown and set the stops. The blade should just touch the outside edge of the mortise on the left and the right.

To make the cuts, slide the jig to one stop, clamp it in place and make the first cut. Then slide the jig to the other stop, and make the second cut.

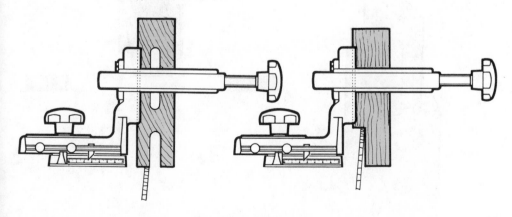

Angled Tenons

To cut tenons at an angle, first cut the ends of the boards off at the desired angle. Then, tilt the saw table to match this angle. This way the end of the board will run flat on the saw table. One side of the tenon on each piece will have to be cut first, and then the saw height re-adjusted to make sure that the shoulder on the other side is at the same height. Finally, cut the cheeks on the second side of each piece.

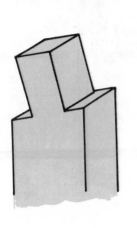

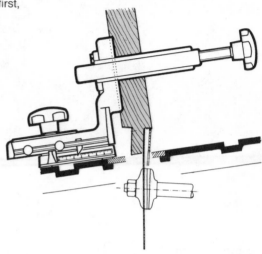

Bevel Shoulder Tenons

These are cut by tilting the top of the workpiece forward before clamping in place. To make this setting easier, make a block at the correct angle and screw it to the back of the tenon jig.

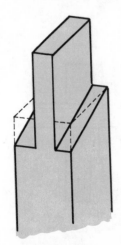

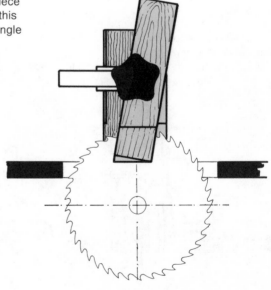

Cutting An Open Mortise and Tenon

With just one setting on the tenon device, an open mortise and tenon can be made. Make a piece of wood the same thickness as the saw cut ("a"). Place a board in the tenon jig and set the jig to make a cut 1/3 of the way in from the edge. Set the left side stop. Make the first cut at this setting. Turn the board around and cut the other side at the same setting. Clear out the middle with several passes.

Lock the jig at the left stop again and clamp the tenon piece in place with the wooden shim beside it. Make one cut, flip the board around and make the next cut. The shim displaces the board to the right the same distance as the thickness of the saw cut. As a result, the tenon and the open mortise are a perfect match. The shoulders of the tenon should be cut off using the mitre guide.

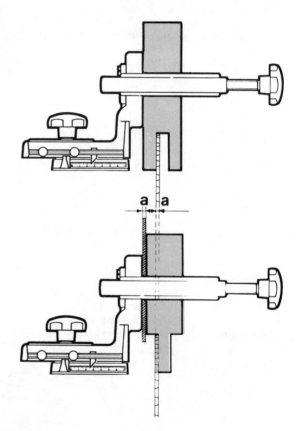

Open Mortises Can be Made in Three Ways

1. By a series of passes.
2. With one pass of a dado or grooving blade.
3. In one pass, using a blade with wobble washers.

Single Dovetails

A single dovetail is a very effective structural joint. It is used primarily to make frames that have to resist being pulled apart.

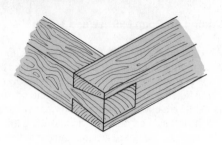

Before you begin to cut, lay the pieces side by sides and mark a line on their faces. This line should be as far from the end as the boards are thick (see a = a). It is better to mark this line with a sharp knife than a pencil line. The knife line will be easier to see and will help prevent tear out.

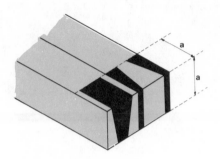

The tenon will be cut first. This can be done in two ways.

With the Tenon Jig

First, cut the shoulders using the mitre guide. Then, tilt the table to 10 degrees and clamp the board in the tenon jig. Make one cut, then turn the board 180 degrees in the tenon device and make the second cut.

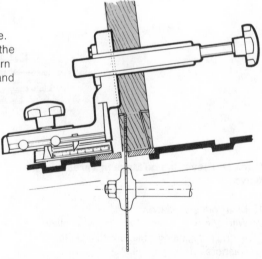

Using the Mitre Guide and Finger Joint Attachment

Replace the normal mitre face with the wooden finger joint attachment. Clamp a block to the wooden face and check with a square to make sure that it is exactly square with the table. Set the table angle to 10 degrees. Adjust the blade height as required. Hold the board to be cut against the block and slide the wooden face left or right until the correct position is obtained. Lock the face and clamp the work to the face. Make the first cut, reverse the piece, make the second cut. Remember to remove the sguare before cutting.

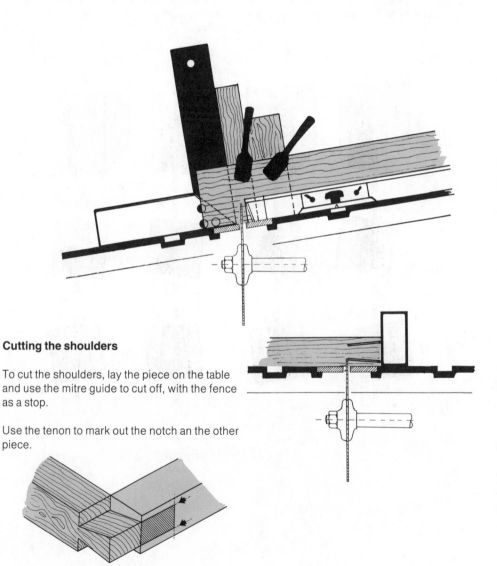

Cutting the shoulders

To cut the shoulders, lay the piece on the table and use the mitre guide to cut off, with the fence as a stop.

Use the tenon to mark out the notch an the other piece.

Cutting the Notch

1. Clamp the second piece to the block on the wooden fence, as described for the tenon.

2. Set the mitre guide at 80 degrees.

3. Loosen the wooden fence so that it can slide, and set it so that the outer edge of the blade is just inside the inner edge of the mark for the notch. Make the first cut.

4. Change the mitre guide setting to 82 degrees for the second cut, 84 degrees for the third and 86 degrees for the fourth cut.

5. Now, change the protractor to the opposite 80 degree position and repeat this series of cuts, ending again with 86 degrees.

If the tenon is too large, set the mitre guide at the 80 degree position and move the wooden fence slightly to take off a very small amount of additional material until you have a good fit.

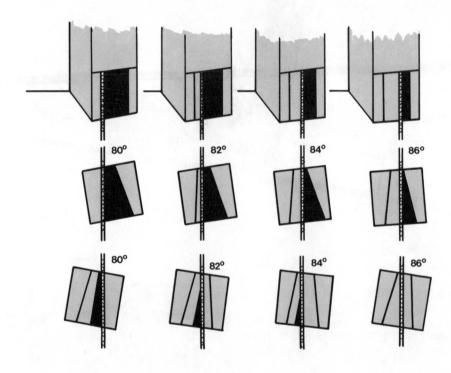

Finger Joints

Finger Joints are used for boxes and drawers and are often left exposed as part of the design of the finished piece. Because of the large amount of gluing area, they are very strong. They can be made easily on the table saw.

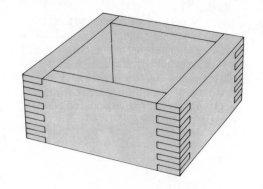

The stock selected for finger joints should be thickness-planed flat and parallel and cut off into four pièces, numbered one through four. The depth of the fingers should equal the thickness of the stock. A knife line should be made at this distance from the end of each board.
This knife line will make set up easier and will also prevent tearout.

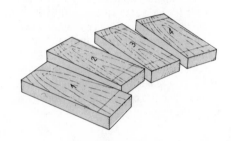

The finger joint attachment consists of a wooden face with a special fitting on the back to slide onto the mitre guide head in place of the ordinary fence. A small pin protrudes on the front of the attachment. This controls the width of the cut. To make these cuts, a dado or grooving blade will be used.

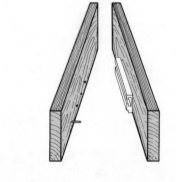

The mitre guide head should be set a 90 degrees for this entire operation.

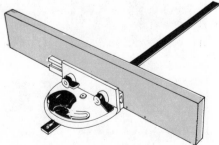

Place the finger joint attachment so that pin is to the right of the blade.
Slide the attachment left or until the distance from the pin to the side of the blade equals the width of the saw cut. (a = a) For example, if the saw cut is 3/8", then the distance between the side of the blade and the pin would be 3/8" - Lock the attachment in place.

Set the depth of cut to equal the thickness of the stock. Hold the side of the first board against the pin. Make the first cut, making certain that you cut all the way through the wooden fence of the attachment. Now, place the opening made by the first cut over the pin and press against the side of the pin. Make the second cut. Each cut is made by placing the pin against the side of the cut just completed.

Its a good idea to make a trial fit with scrap stock before making cuts in your good boards. If the fit is too loose, shift the finger joint attachment to the right. If it's too tight, shift to the left.

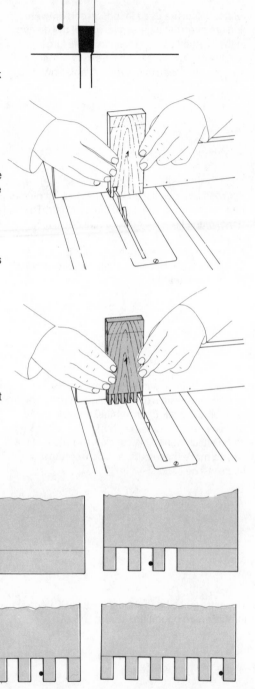

When you have finished cutting all the fingers on one end, turn the board upside down and cut the fingers for the other end. Remember to start from the same edge of the board.

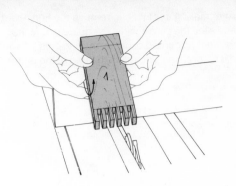

Follow this same procedure for two of the four sides. For the remaining two sides the starting point will be different.

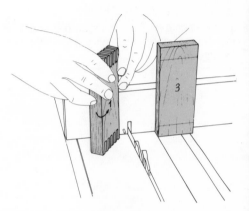

Turn one of the first pieces over and hook the first finger cut over the guide pin. Press the side of the third piece to be cut against the side of the first. In this way the first cut will be at the very edge – an opening that will mate exactly with the first finger of the adjoining board.

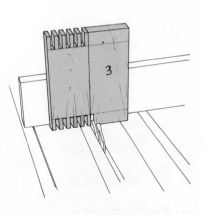

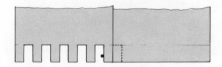

After making this first cut, remove the first board and slide the third against the guide pin. Make the second cut and continue making cuts, as you did before, until you reach the end of the board.

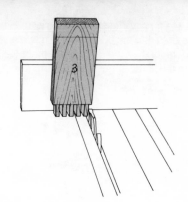

Turn the board over, put space here and follow the same procedure for the other ends and again for the fourth side.

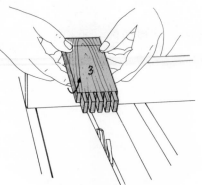

Dovetail Drawer Joints

This is the strongest joint for corners of drawers or boxes and is very attractive. Often, it is left exposed. This joint can be made easily and accurately on the table saw using only the mitre guide, a finger joint attachment with the guide pin removed, and a series of wooden spacer blocks made from scrap wood.

The spacer blocks should be cut from a stick that has been thickness planed to the reguired width. Then, each block will be exactly the same width as its neighbors and very accurate work can be done.

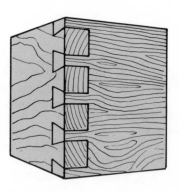

Tails and Pins

Planed distance blocks determine the tenon width.

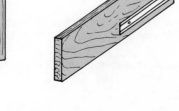

The metal rail on the fence will be moved to the right.

Cutting The Tails

To illustrate this process, we will cut dovetails on a 4-1/4" wide board.

The blocks will be used to space the cuts along the width of the piece. To figure out how wide your blocks should be, first decide how many tails you want. Then, subtract 1/4" from the width of your finished workpiece. This allows for a 1/4" pin at either end of the board. Finally, divide this number by the number of tails, the result is the width of the guide blocks. In our example: We will use four (4) tails. The total width is 4-1/4" less 1/4" for the end pins leaves 4". Divided by 4 tails leaves blocks each 1" wide.

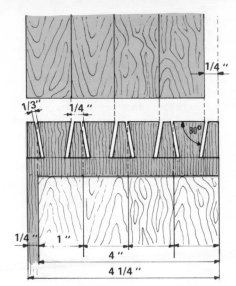

After preparing the blocks you must prepare your boards. Using a knife, mark a line across the width of each end of each board. This line should be as far from the end as the board is thick (a = a). This knife cut will help prevent tearout and will be easy to see for set up.

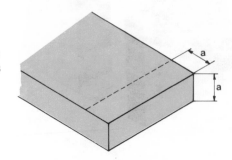

Move the sliding fitting on the back of the finger joint jig to the far right end by removing and relocating the wood screws that hold it in place. Remove the guide pin usually used for finger joint work. It will not be used.

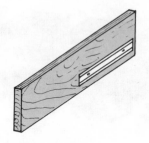

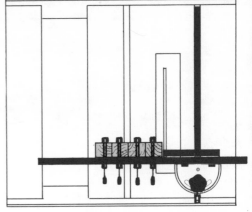

Place the finger joint jig on the mitre guide and place the mitre guide in the right hand slot of the saw table. Set the guide at 90 degrees.

The saw table should be tilted to 10 degrees. This will be the angle of the tails.

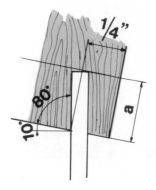

Clamp four blocks to the wooden fence so that the first cut is 1/4" from the end. You will have to first gauge this by eye and clamp the blocks in place and then make final adjustment by sliding the wooden fence to the left and right, making a test cut until you are satisfied.

Now set the depth of cut so that the corner of the blade just touches the scribed line.

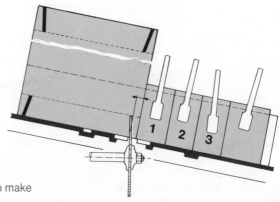

Make the first cut and rotate the board to make one cut just like the first in each corner.

Remove the first block and make the next four cuts against the second block.

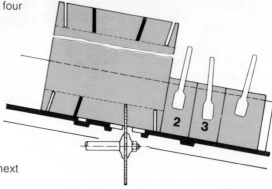

Remove the second block and make the next four cuts.

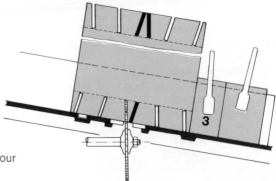

Remove the third block and make the last four cuts.

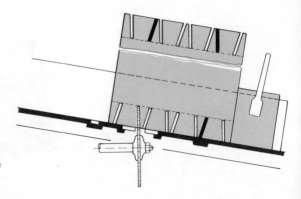

This procedure should be repeated for the opposite side of the box or drawer.

Obviously, using this method it is most efficient to make the same cut on all pieces that are the same dimensions one after another.

After making all the angle cuts in the boards that are to have tails, return the table to its horizontal position. Then reset the wooden fence so that the blade is guided through the center of the waste area. Use the guide blocks to space the blade to each cut.

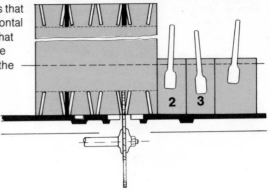

If you do the cleanout right before cutting the mating pins, you can use the grooving or dado blade which will make a wider, cleaner cut than the regular blade.

This is the cut made by the regular blade.

The center cut here was made by a grooving blade.

The final cleanout is done with a chisel. Alternately, use your bandsaw with a 1/8" blade to clean out the corners.

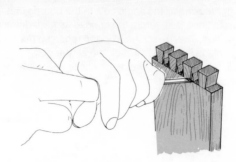

Cutting the Pins

After the dovetails are cut, you can cut the pins to match. You will use exactly the same jig, but this time you will angle the mitre guide instead of the table.

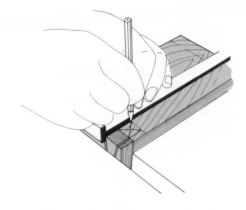

First, you will have to mark up one piece. This is only necessary for the first cut. Once the jig is set up, all similiar pieces can be cut without having to mark each one.

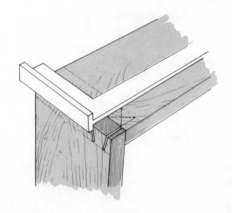

Clamp the tailpiece in a vise with the pin piece in front of it. Lay a square over both pieces and mark the edges of the end tail. Use a very sharp pencil or better, a knife. Make an "X" in between the lines to indicate the waste area.

Place the mitre guide in its slot and angle the head 10 degrees, clockwise. Place the workpiece against the first block.

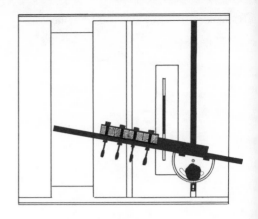

Adjust the wooden fence so that the left corner of the grooving blade is just inside the left side line marked on the front of your first board. This will be your first cut.

For the second cut, rotate the board to the diagonally opposite corner. You can not cut all four corners by this method. First you will work from corner to opposite corner.

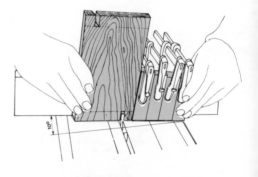

Remove a block, make another cut and then another in the diagonally opposite corner.

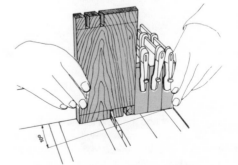

Continue in this way until you are at the last block.

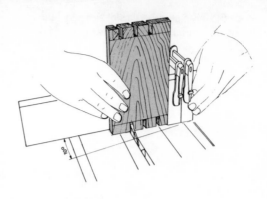

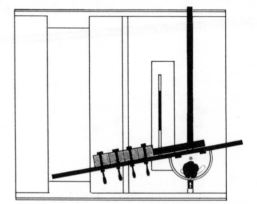

Now, turn the mitre guide head to 10 degrees counterclockwise and set the blocks in place.

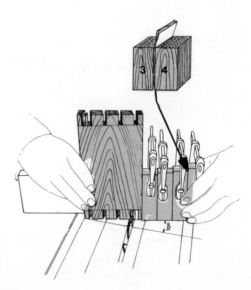

This time, however, add four paper shims between the last and the next to last block. These shims can be ordinary writing paper, cut in strips, with one end tacked to the top of the last block. They will be used for final adjustments.

Place the workpiece in place and line up the right corner of the blade just inside of the right side line on the front of your first board. Make the first cut and then proceed removing blocks and making cuts until you are finished.

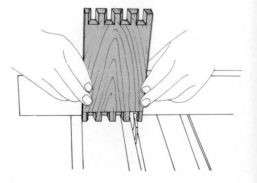

Use a chisel or coping saw to remove the waste from the pins on one board for a trial fitting. Try to fit the joint together. If the joint is too tight, as it may be, remove one of the paper shims. Writing paper is about .004" thick, so when you remove one shim and make the final cuts over again, you will be removing only another .004". When you are satisfied that you have a smooth sliding fit, continue to make the cuts on all the pieces you are working on.

When the pieces are all cut, you can clean out the waste between the pins by changing the angle of the mitre guide to 90 degrees and cutting straight through.

Mouldings

The following accessories are required for moulding operations on the table saw.

A Moulding Head

This special cutterhead is designed to hold a pair of shaped cutters and is mounted on the saw arbor in place of the saw blade. The washer shown next to it is placed between the arbor nut and the moulding head. It's a good idea, if you do a lot of moulding, to have two moulding heads all set up with knives for the most common cuts you do. This will save you the time of changing knives.

The Cutters

Cutters are made up in identical pairs in a large variety of designs. Before the first use, be certain to completely remove the protective varnish coating on the cutter. To sharpen these cutters, always hone the back, flat side, of the cutter on a bench stone. Never try to grind the beveled profile. Leave that work to a professional grinding shop.

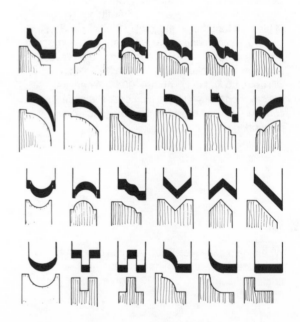

A Wide Slot Table Insert

The narrow slotted table insert, which is made for ordinary sawing, must be replaced with a wide slotted insert which allows the moulding head to pass through.

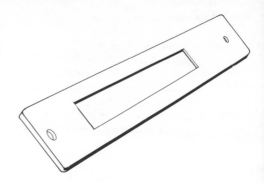

The Moulding Head Cutter Adjuster

The moulding head is placed on the center spindle of this device and one cutter installed. The vertical scale is moved in until it just touches the cutter. The height of the cutter is noted on the scale. The cutterhead is then rotated, the other cutter installed and is set to correspond with the setting of the first.

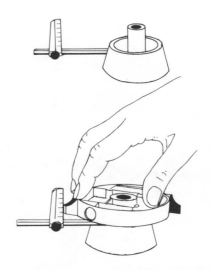

The Moulding Safety Fence

This is a wooden fence which has a curved cutout on its lower edge. It is as thick as the moulding head is wide. You can control exactly how much of the cutter you wish to have exposed by bolting this to the rip fence.

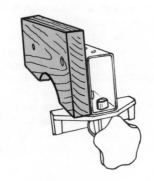

The Safety Hold-down

Two pressure feet hold the work firmly down against the table and in against the fence. The safety hold-down is bolted to the table, either on the left or right side, through holes bored outside the mitre guide slots. Using this device will keep your hands clear of the blade, prevent kickback, and give you a very clean cut.

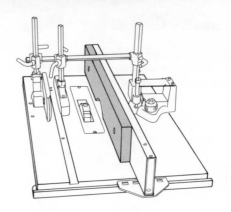

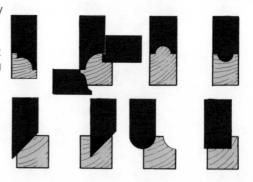

Decorative Moulding

By making several passes, using different shaped cutters, you can create an endless variety of mouldings. You can tilt the saw table to make even more kinds of mouldings. Make a few test cuts on scrap to determine which side to cut first to eliminate tearout. Most often, you will cut along the long grain first and then across the end grain. The first operation may produce a little tearout, but the second should eliminate it. Also, in particularly hard woods, you may have to take several passes, gradually increasing the depth of cut. This is for safety and for the best surface finish.

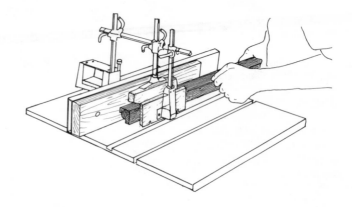

Mortising

The mortising table is mounted on the saw facing the drill chuck. This table is designed to give you control of the workpieces in three directions: height, infeed/outfeed, crossfeed. Also, the table is designed to be tilted up as much as 90 degrees for angled mortises. Clamps are provided to hold the work in place and stops are used to correctly position each board in a series of identical pieces.

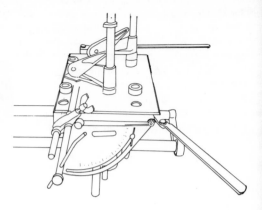

Mortising Cutters

Two types are available: mortise drills (top) and mortise miller bits (lower). The mortise drill is used to bore a series of overlapping holes to full depth and clear out the remaining waste by crossfeeding. The miller bit is fed into the work a small amount (1/16" - 1/8") and then crossfed from left to right. The miller bit generally has a larger shank, is stiffer and generally cuts a smoother mortise.

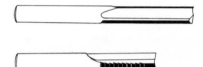

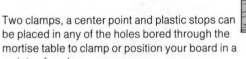

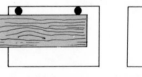

Making Mortises

Two clamps, a center point and plastic stops can be placed in any of the holes bored through the mortise table to clamp or position your board in a variety of angles.

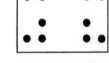

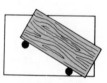

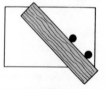

Mark out the length of your mortise on the edge of the board with a pencil and clamp it in place. First adjust the table to the correct height, set the crossfeed stops to limit the left to right movement, and finally set the infeed stop for the depth of the cut. The side stop rod is used as a positioning stop for mass production. The mortise is made by moving the two control levers. Work smoothly, without rushing, for the best result.

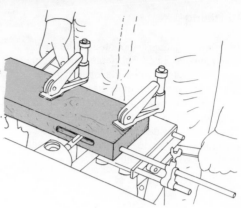

Angled Mortises

With the table tilted, an angled mortise is cut just like a straight one. The plastic stops keep the board from sliding off the table.

Square Holes

Square holes can be cut straight or angled. They are made by cutting a mortise and then raising (or lowering) the mortise table slightly and cutting another mortise.

Through Mortises

If you are going to cut a through mortise with the table tilted, place a piece of scrap wood underneath it, or clamp it on top of the plastic stops. Standard screw clamps can also be used to hold work to the mortise table if necessary.

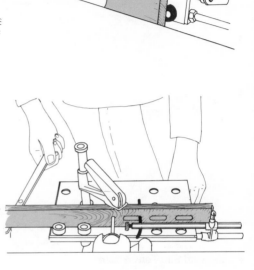

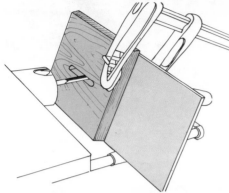

Even Spacing

When you have to make a series of close, evenly spaced mortises, use the stop finger as shown. Place the stop finger inside, and at the end of, the first mortise to cut the next. The exact distance will be set by initial measurement, of course.

Grooves for Shutters or Stair Treads

For this operation, the table will be tilted at 90 degrees to its normal position. The angle of the grooves can be maintained by using the plastic stops or by using a block of wood cut at the desired angle as a guide.

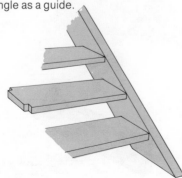

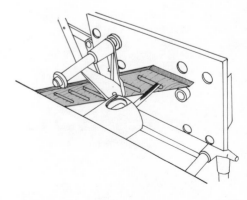

Other Applications

The mortise table can also be used with an electric hand drill in a special holder, or by another power source.

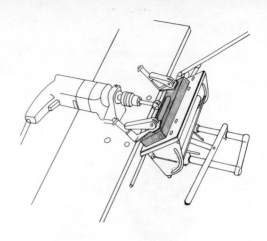

Mortise and Slip Tenon Joint

Both sides of a mitred frame have to be mortised for this joint. After making both mortises, cut a small tongue to hold them together. Glue the joint. For the best results, the mortises should be absolutely centered.

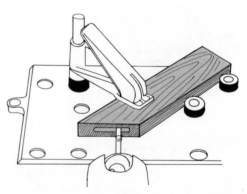

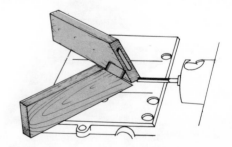

Making Dowel Holes

For a right angle joint, use a wooden block as shown to act as a stop for both sides of the joint. Be sure to center the hole precisely in the board. Set the crossfeed stops to drill the two holes, one on either side of the joint. Drill the first piece as shown at right, the second as shown below.

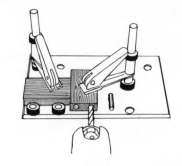

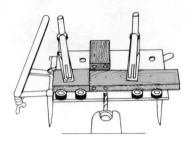

When drilling dowel holes into mitred corners, use two of the plastic stops to achieve a 45 degree angle easily.

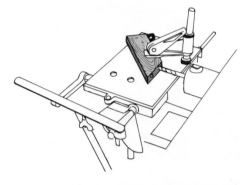

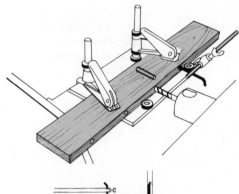

The stop finger can be used to space dowel holes for edge-joining lumber. Drill the first hole about 2" from the end of the board. Slide the board over and place the stop finger in the hole. Adjust the distance from the stop in the first hole to the drill for the second hole. Clamp the stop in place and drill the second hole. Now the stop is set. You only have to slide the board down and place the freshly drilled hole over the stop finger.

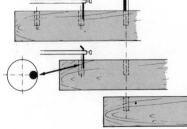

Wedged Through Tenons

For a through, wedged tenon, you will make a mortise that is approximately 1/8" wider at the top or outside than at the bottom. The tenon should have two slots cut across its width. After inserting the tenon, drive the wedges in the slots. Use glue sparingly. This joint is very strong even without glue.

Blind Wedged Tenons

The same type of joint described above can be made without the tenon end being exposed. For the blind wedged tenon, the mortise should be slightly wider at the bottom. The tenon, mortise and wedges must all be the same length. Do not make the wedges too fat at their wide end, or you will never be able to drive the tenon home. Practice this one on scrap stock — once you drive the tenon home, you will never get this joint apart again!

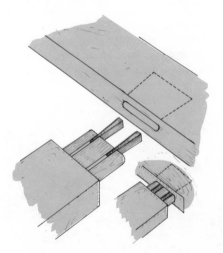

Sanding with the Table Saw

A sanding disc or sanding drum can be installed in the chuck mounted in front of a mortise table.

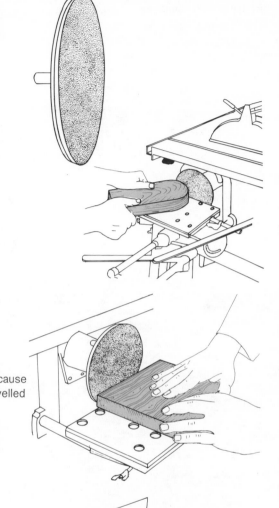

Freehand sanding on the mortise table. Because the table can be tilted, you can also sand bevelled surfaces, edges or chamfers.

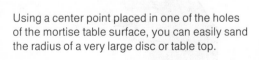

Using a center point placed in one of the holes of the mortise table surface, you can easily sand the radius of a very large disc or table top.

By tilting the table in conjunction with the center point, you can chamfer the edge of the same disc.

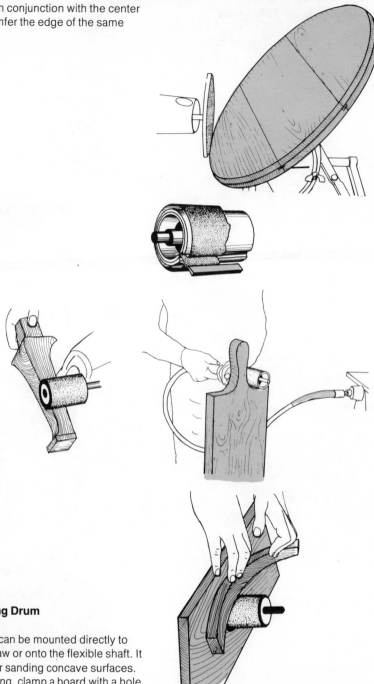

Using The Sanding Drum

The sanding drum can be mounted directly to the chuck on the saw or onto the flexible shaft. It is used primarily for sanding concave surfaces. To do angled sanding, clamp a board with a hole bored through it to the mortise table.

Dust Collection

A dust collector can be connected to every machine in the shop, with an appropriate hood. Not only does it keep the workshop clean, it also reduces the amount of air borne particles that you inhale.

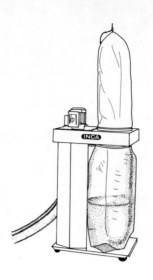

Using the Bandsaw

Blade selection, technique, accessories

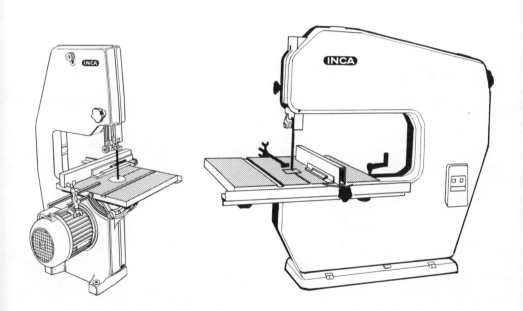

Bandsaw Blades

It's a good idea to have on hand a wide variety of blades for various types of cuts in different materials.

Always reset the blade guides, following the instructions in your owner manual, each time you change blades.

The blades shown below are representative of the types commonly available. Your dealer may stock other blades in addition.

Metric specifications are shown first, followed by imperial sizes.

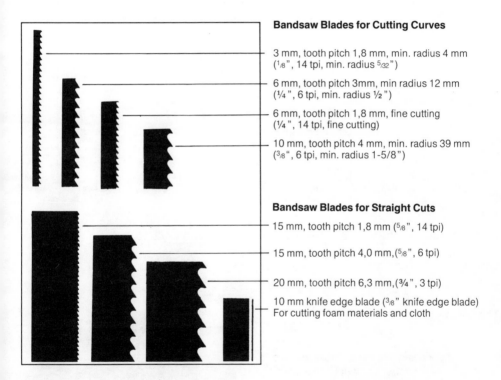

Bandsaw Blades for Cutting Curves

3 mm, tooth pitch 1,8 mm, min. radius 4 mm ($\frac{1}{8}$", 14 tpi, min. radius $\frac{5}{32}$")

6 mm, tooth pitch 3mm, min radius 12 mm ($\frac{1}{4}$", 6 tpi, min. radius $\frac{1}{2}$")

6 mm, tooth pitch 1,8 mm, fine cutting ($\frac{1}{4}$", 14 tpi, fine cutting)

10 mm, tooth pitch 4 mm, min. radius 39 mm ($\frac{3}{8}$", 6 tpi, min. radius 1-5/8")

Bandsaw Blades for Straight Cuts

15 mm, tooth pitch 1,8 mm ($\frac{5}{8}$", 14 tpi)

15 mm, tooth pitch 4,0 mm, ($\frac{5}{8}$", 6 tpi)

20 mm, tooth pitch 6,3 mm, ($\frac{3}{4}$", 3 tpi)

10 mm knife edge blade ($\frac{3}{8}$" knife edge blade) For cutting foam materials and cloth

These blades, except the knife edge blade, may be used for both wood and non-ferrous metals. However, there are many different types of tooth forms manufactured to suit specific materials. Consult with your dealer for his recommendation.

A Guide For Bandsaw Blade Selection

Type of cut	Blade Teeth	Width	Feed Speed	Blade Speed
Wood:				
Thick Stock	Coarse	Wide	Slow	Medium
Thin Stock	Fine	Medium	Medium	Medium
Gradual Curves	Medium	Medium	Slow	Medium
Sharp Curves	Fine	Narrow	Slow	Medium
Ripping	Medium	Wide	Medium	Medium
Cross Cutting	Medium	Wide	Medium	Medium
Mitre Cutting	Medium	Wide	Medium	Medium
Tenons & Slots	Medium	Medium	Slow	Medium
Round Stock	Medium	Medium	Slow	Medium
Hardboard	Medium	Medium	Slow	Low
Plastics:				
Thick	Coarse	Medium	Slow	Low
Thin	Medium	Medium	Medium	Low
Foam Materials:				
Hard	Medium	Medium	Fast	Medium
Soft	Knife Band	–	Medium	Medium
Paper, Cardboard	Knife Band	–	Medium	Medium
Non-Ferrous Metal	Fine	Wide	Slow	Low
Sanding	–	–	Medium	High

Blades: Narrow: 1/16" to 1/8"   Medium: 1/4" to 3/8"   Wide: 1/2" to 3/4"

The Best Cut

To get the best cut, at least three teeth should be in the stock being cut. For example, to cut a piece of 1" thick lumber you would need a blade with at least 3 teeth per inch. You could use a finer blade but never a coarser one. This means: select a fine blade for thin stock and a coarse tooth blade to cut thick stock. A coarse blade allows the teeth to clear the wood chips and dust easily and quickly as you cut. This is particularly important when cutting wet lumber, where a fine blade would tend to jam in the cut.

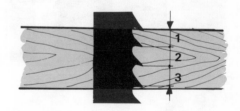

If, for some reason, it is neccessary to use a fine blade to cut thick stock, be sure to feed the work into the blade very slowly. This allows enough time for all the sawdust to be ejected from the cut.

The Set of the Teeth of
The Bandsaw Blade

To allow enough room for the body of the bandsaw blade to pass through the cut, the teeth are "set". That means each tooth is pushed alternately left and right. This also allows the blade to cut curves as illustrated.
You must select the right blade for the job. A sharp curve with a small radius will require a narrow blade. A more gradual curve with a larger radius can be made with a wider blade.

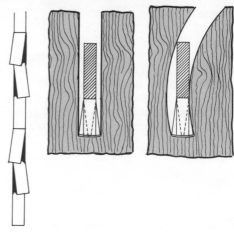

This table shows the radius of a curve that you can cut with commonly available blades.

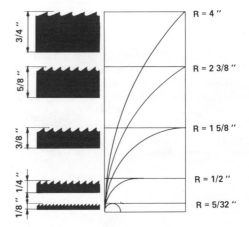

Poor Bandsaw Cuts and
Their Causes

Blade wanders during ripping

Possible Reasons:
- The blade selected is too narrow.
- The tooth pattern is too fine (too many teeth per inch).
- The blade guides are not set correctly.
- There is not enough tension on the blade.
- The teeth are not set enough.
- The teeth are not evenly set.
- The wood is fed too quickly into the blade.
- The blade speed is too low.
- The upper blade guide is not close enough to the wood.

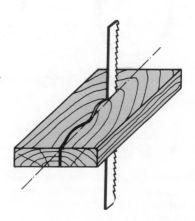

The barrel cut

The barrel cut sometimes occurs when cutting
thick stock or resawing. The reasons for this
fault are the same as described above.
In addition, this can also be caused if the rip
fence is not set parallel to the saw cut. The rip
fence can be readjusted, using the screws that
hold the fence bar to the fence clamp casting.

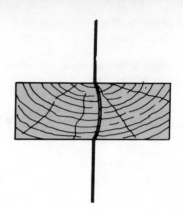

Storage and Maintenance of Blades

It's a good idea to reduce the tension on the
bandsaw blade if the machine will not be used
for longer than overnight.

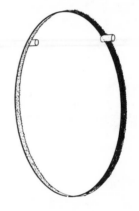

Spare blades should be brushed clean and
coated with a thin film of light oil before storage to
prevent rust. The spare blades should be
hung on two wooden pegs on the wall to prevent
"kinks" or bends. If you do not have enough
space for this, the blades can be rolled into
"loops".- There are several techniques for
rolling blades, here is one:

Be careful when handling bandsaw
blades! Use gloves and be sure that the teeth
are pointing away from you.

Hold the blade with both hands. The teeth should
face away from you and your thumbs should be
behind the back of the blade, facing up.

Bend the upper half of the blade down towards the floor using your thumbs, through the lower half.

Bring your hands together and cross the two loops. Do not let the blade "kink" or bend in this procedure.

Sometimes you will buy a blade whose teeth are pointed in the wrong direction. In that case, turn the blade inside out as shown in the illustration.

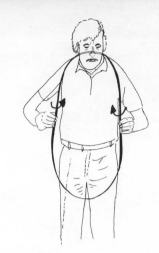

Freehand Cutting

The blade guides, both above and below the table, must be set correctly. If you are not sure how to set your guides, consult your owners manual or your dealer.
The upper blade guide can be raised and lowered. It should always be no higher than $3/8$" from the top of the work being cut. This way you will have the shortest possible distance between the upper and lower guides, which will help you make the best possible cut. This helps cover the blade, reducing the risk of an accident.

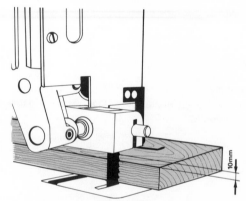

Cutting With a Very Narrow Blade

Very intricate patterns can be cut with blades $1/16$" or $1/8$" wide.

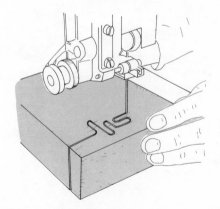

This puzzle illustrates an interlocking cut made through the face and the edge of a board.

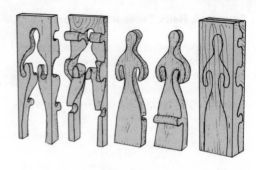

A Straight Freehand Crosscut

First, mark the cut with a pencil and a try square. Guide the board straight into the blade following the pencil line. Use both hands to hold and guide the board.

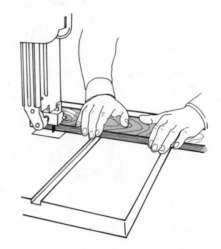

Cutting Large Panels

To cut large panels, you must stand in front of the blade with one hand on each side of the saw cut. Smoothly feed the panel into the blade pressing outwards, as illustrated by the arrows, to prevent the cut from closing on and jamming the blade. For this work, a set of extension rails and an extension table installed on your saw will make the work much easier.

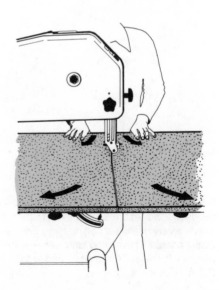

Extension, Rails, Table and Support

A set of extension rails and extension table are
available for the INCA 20" bandsaw as
accessories. These can be installed to the left, or
behind blade. The support leg is adjustable in
height so that you can tilt the table for mitre cuts.

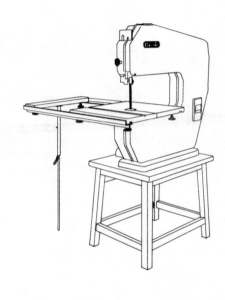

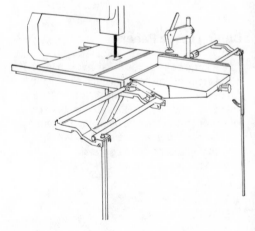

A sliding table is also available for the INCA 20"
bandsaw. This features a clamping mitre guide
which is very useful for cutting large panels or
heavy boards. This sliding table can also be
attached to the INCA table saw and to the
INCA shaper.

Internal Cuts

When the waste is on the outside of a board, you can easily make right angle corners with two straight cuts, one from each side of the piece. If the corners and waste are on the inside of the board, as shown here, several cuts will be made.

First, carefully lay out the cutting lines.

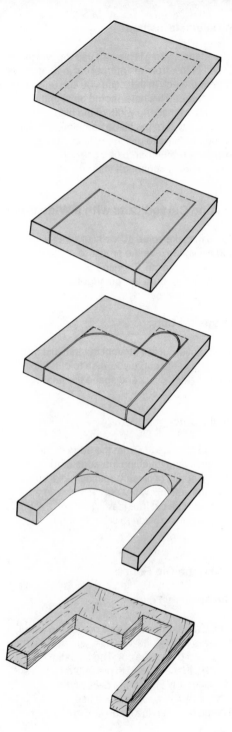

Make two straight cuts, one along each side, right to the corners. Pull back slowly and carefully so as not to pull the blade off the bandwheels.

Now, using an appropriate blade for the curve required, cut away most of the waste.

With the waste removed as shown, you will easily be able to make the remaining straight cuts to clear the corners.

The completed piece has clear, sharp corners.

An alternate method

Sometimes, you will have to use the waste, or cut off piece, from an internal cut in another part of your project. In that case you can drill a hole at each corner. This hole should be slightly larger in diameter than the width of the blade. It will allow you to turn the blade completely at each corner. Be sure to drill the hole in the waste area, and remember to go back after the waste is removed to square off the corners.

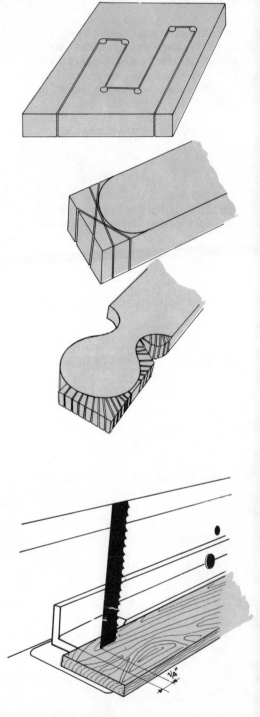

Making Curved Cuts with a Wide Blade

You can make some curved cuts with a wide blade if you relieve the pressure of the wood on one side of the cut. Then the back of the blade will not jam or burn as you negotiate the curves. There are two methods:

Tangential Cuts

A tangential cut is a straight cut that just touches the edge of the curve you wish to cut. Make a series of these cuts and shape the final curve last.

Radial Cuts

A radial cut extends from the edge of the board straight in and touching the edge of the curve. Make a series of closely spaced radial cuts first. Then, as you follow the curve, these small pieces will be cut free leaving plenty of room for the body of the blade to pass through.

Using the Rip Fence

The Auxiliary Fence

Sometimes, when ripping a board, the wood will open around the saw kerf, jam against the fence and distort the cut. The adjustable auxiliary fence is used to prevent this. It is set with its end 1/2" past the back of the blade. Then, after the wood is cut, it has room to expand between the blade and main fence.

Cutting Veneers and Thin Stock

The main fence has rounded corners which will not support very thin pieces. In these cases, make up a wooden face for your fence out of a piece of dry, parallel-planed hardwood. There are holes provided in the main fence to bolt or screw special faces to your fence. Be sure that this face rests flat on the table for cutting veneers.

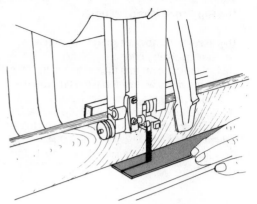

Resawing Wide Boards

The standard main fence is really not tall enough to properly support wide boards. Again, make up a hardwood face for your fence. For this purpose, the face should be as high as the boards you will be resawing. Be sure that the wooden fence is planed flat and, when installed, is at right angles to the table top.

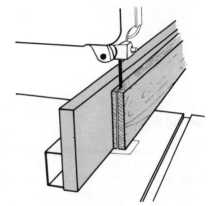

Sawing Small Logs

To saw small logs, plane two sides of the quartered log at right angles to each other. Then, saw off planks of the thickness you need. Use a wide, coarse blade for this operation and feed slowly. If the interior of the log is still wet or "green", as it is likely to be, the blade will probably jam in the cut. As soon as it begins to jam, shut off the machine. Then drive some wedges into the cut. Switch on the machine and complete your cut.

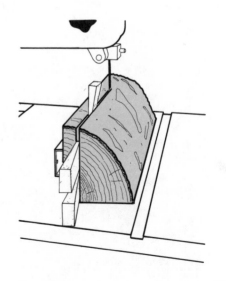

The Rip Fence Micro Adjuster

This accessory provides extremely precise adjustment of the rip fence. To use it, thread the shaft of the adjuster into the casting of the fence. Clamp the micro adjuster and the fence to the table rail. Loosen the main fence clamp slightly. Rotate the knurled knob to move the fence left or right. Each of the graduation marks on the left side of the knurled wheel equals 0.004". Be sure to tighten the main fence clamp before cutting.

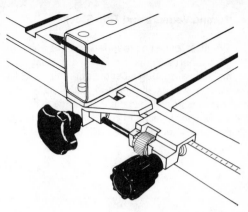

Sawing Bevels

To rip a bevel on the bandsaw, you tilt the table to the angle required, place the fence on the "downhill" side (below the blade) and cut as you would normally.

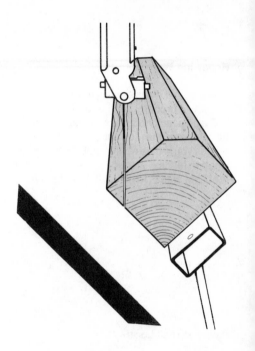

Cutting Tenons

The tenon is a very strong and attractive joint.
It is easily cut on the bandsaw using the rip
fence, mitre guide and depth stop.

First, mark out the tenon. The width of the tenon
is usually 1/3 of the width of the board.

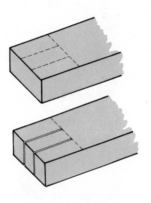

Next, using the rip fence as a guide and the
depth stop as a limit, make the long cuts. Work
to the outside of the pencil line.

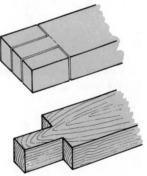

Finally, use the mitre guide, set at 90 degrees,
to cut the shoulders of the tenon. Use the depth
stop on the saw and the length stop on the
mitre guide.

To cut the mating slot for the tenon, mark out
your board as you did for the tenon.

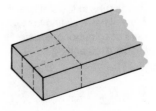

Use the rip fence and stop to make the straight cuts. This time, however, cut to the inside of the pencil line.

To remove the waste, make two freehand ·curved cuts. The balance of the waste, at the bottom of the cut, can be removed with a chisel or with the bandsaw using a very narrow blade, for example the 1/8" blade.

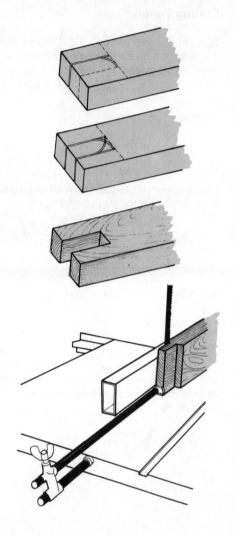

The Depth Stop

This stop is very useful, especially for repetative cuts for tenons, notches, etc.

The Mitre Guide

The mitre guide runs in the slot milled in the bandsaw table. It has a sliding face, adjustable drop stop and a protractor graduated from 90 to 45 degrees to the left and right.

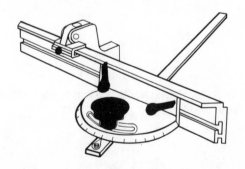

Right Angels Cuts

90 degree cuts are made with the sliding face positioned as close to the blade as possible. Hold the work firmly against the face and cut smoothly.

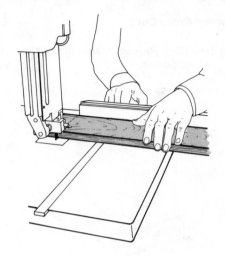

The Adjustable Drop Stop

This stop is invaluable for multiple cutoff work. It can be positioned anywhere along the sliding face of the mitre guide and locked in place. Flip it up to make one end of your board square. Then, lower the stop and place the square end of your board against it to cut off pieces of equal length.

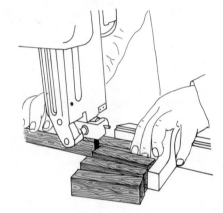

Cutting an Angled Mitre

Adjust the protractor head of the mitre guide to the desired angle, and proceed as for a right angle cut. Be sure that the sliding face will not be cut by the blade!

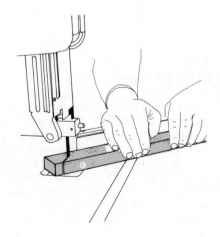

A Bevelled Cross Cut

By tilting the table, you can make a right angle cut with a beveled end.

Compound Mitres

By tilting the table and changing the angle of the mitre guide protractor head you can cut compound bevels

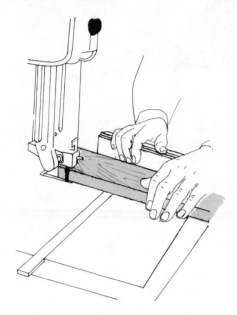

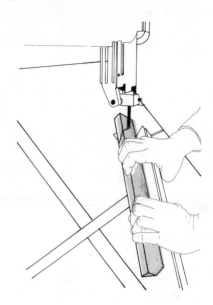

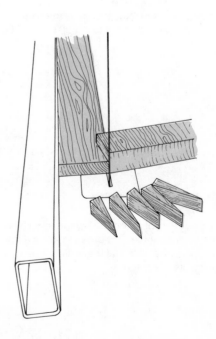

Cutting Wedges

Small wedges can be easily cut by making up a sliding jig out of scrap wood. The jig has a small wedge shaped notch formed on one side, close to the end. The side of the jig slides along the rip fence and the piece to be cut is placed in the notch. By flipping the board over after each cut, identical wedges can be cut. The strongest wedges have the grain of the wood running along the length of the wedge.

Push Sticks and Hold-In Jigs

Push sticks, blocks and hold-in jigs prevent accidents. The simplest hold-in is a finger board, which is just a piece of scrap wood with a series of closely spaced slots cut into it. This is clamped to the bandsaw table so that the "fingers" press against the side of the board being cut.

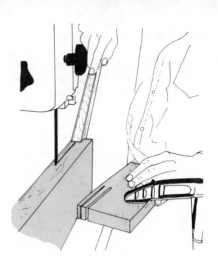

Out of scrap wood, make up several push sticks and blocks for ripping and resawing. Also, make a pointed wooden stick to push little cutoff pieces away from the blade. NEVER try to blow them away or brush them with your hand while the saw is running.

Sawing Tapers

The simplest taper jig is simply a notch cut out of a board. It is used to cut tapers on only one side of a board by placing the board to be cut in the notch and sliding the jig along the rip fence.

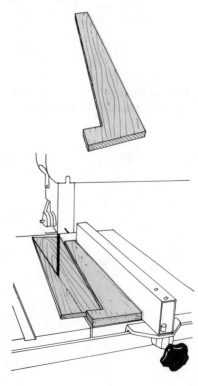

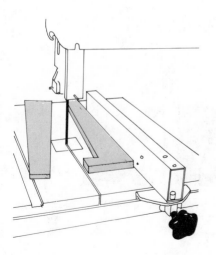

Double Sided Tapers

With a slight change the jig just described can cut two tapers, one on each side of a board. To do this, your jig will have two stops for the board to rest on.

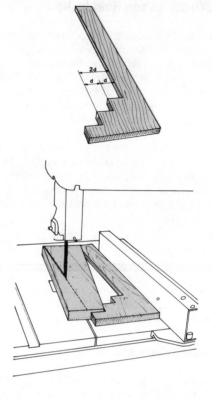

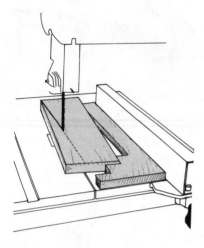

The first, marked "d" will form one side of the taper. Flip the board over and place the just cut edge against the second corner, "2d", to make the second cut.

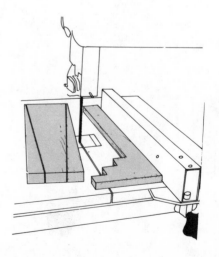

An Adjustable Taper Jig

With a hinge, two boards and a little ingenuity, you can make your own adjustable taper jig. This device is described on p. 28.

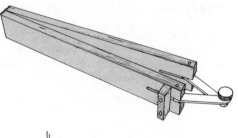

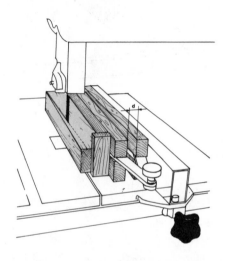

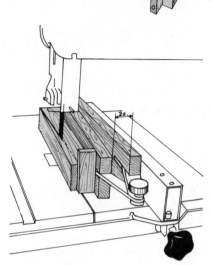

The first cut will be made with a measurment "d" between the two ends.

The second cut will be made by flipping the board over 180 degrees and doubling the distance between the ends of the taper jig.

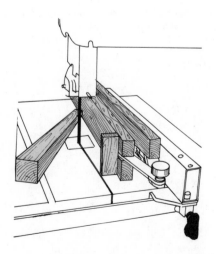

The sequence of cuts to make a furniture leg that is tapered on all four sides is described on p. 28 – 29, with the formula used to calculate tapers.

Cutting Logs or Round Pieces

Large Pieces

To rip a large, round log you must clamp two
boards with 45 degree bevelled edges to the
table on each side of the blade. These will form
a groove for the log to ride in as it is cut.

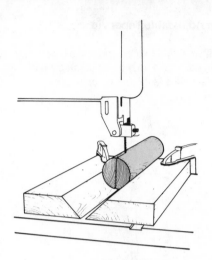

Ripping Dowels

Small round rods must have a more secure jig
to hold them and to prevent them from
rotating as you cut.

Cut a "v" shaped groove in the top of a block
of wood. Cut a saw notch in the back of this
piece and install a thin metal, wood, or stiff
plastic strip in the notch. This strip will be behind
the blade and will prevent the work from
turning. Then, make another cut so that you can
insert the blade halfway through the block and
clamp the block to the table as shown.

Slowly feed the wooden dowel into the blade
until it reaches the guide strip behind. Then you
can feed at a normal feed rate.

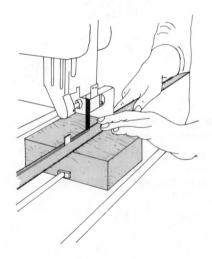

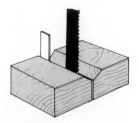

Crosscutting Round Stock

You must use a jig or holder to crosscut round stock.

One is simply a wedge with the sharp points of several nails or screws protruding from its surface, used as shown.

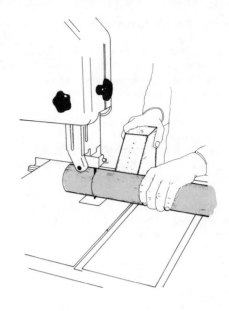

Another one, which is better, is a "V" groove jig with several screw points protruding at the bottom of the "V". This can be used with the mitre guide behind it to produce the most accurate crosscuts of round stock.

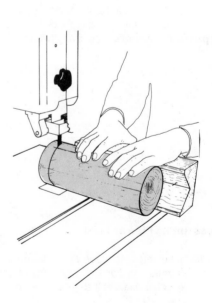

Cutting Spiral Grooves in Dowels

Spiral grooves are made in dowels to allow
excess glue and air to escape when assembling
dowelled joints. These grooves are easily
cut on the bandsaw using the mitre guide.

Clamp the mitre guide to the table so that the
blade will cut a grooves 1/32" deep in the dowel
you will be using. Move the sliding face of the
mitre guide to the right so that it will support the
dowel both before and after it is cut.

Tilt the table to between 15 and 30 degrees.
This angle will determine the pitch of the spiral
you will cut.

Feed the dowel down the face of the mitre guide
until it reaches the blade. Continue feeding and
turning the dowel in the same direction as
shown by the arrows in the illustration.

Be careful to keep your hands and fingers away
from the blade, controlling the cut by holding
the part of the dowel farthest away from the
blade.

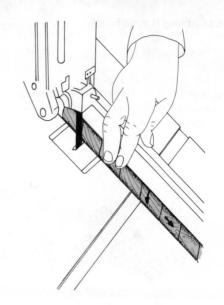

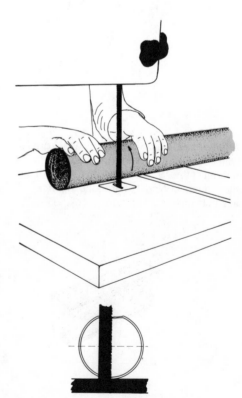

Crosscutting Pipe or Tube

Thinwall pipe or tubing made of cardboard
plastic, aluminum or nonferrous metals can be
cut with your bandsaw at the lowest speed,
using a fine blade.

After you begin the cut, slowly rotate the pipe in
the direction shown by the arrow. If you do not
rotate the pipe for this cut, it is likely to jam the
blade or tear the pipe when you have cut halfway
through.

Cutting Rolls of Cardboard or Paper

This cut should be done the same way
as for crosscutting a log, but use a very fine
blade and feed slowly and carefully.

Cutting other materials

If you have to cut insulation, panels,
old lumber or other materials, check carefully
for foreign matter such as pebbles, nails
screws or sand. Any of this could ruin a
bandsaw blade.

Cross-Cutting Long Boards

When you must have a cut that is farther from
either end of the board than the depth of the
bandsaw throat, you must use this special
technique.

Stand the board on edge and cut through beside
your layout mark on the edge. This cut will not
be square, so you will have to make a second
cut to square it off.

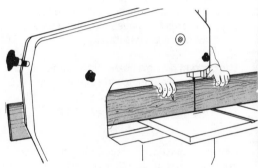

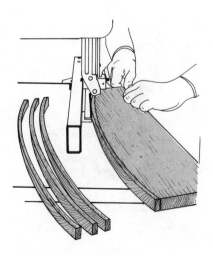

Copying Curves

To make several pieces with the same curve,
layout the curve on a wide board and cut this
curve freehand. Then, set the rip fence, with the
auxiliary fence attached, to the width of the
board needed.

Following the original curve, you can cut out
one piece after another with the same curved
shape.

Copying Complex Curves

For wavy, or "S" shaped curves you will follow
the same procedure just outlined except that
instead of using the rip fence as a guide, you
will use a board with a rounded end as shown.
This board is clamped to the table so that the
space between the rounded end and the blade is
the width of the finished piece required.

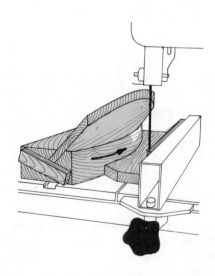

Bevelled Curves

A bevelled curve is often used in cooperage,
boat building and for chair backs. It can easily
be cut on the band saw using a simple
two-part jig.

The first part is a curved template that rests on
the bandsaw table and against the rip fence.
This template must have on opening for the
bandsaw blade to pass through.

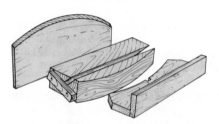

The second part is a heavy block with a curve
cut on one side to match the curve of the
template. It also must have a groove cut
in the top at the angle needed for the
bevel.

A board is placed in the groove on the block.
You will then slide the block around the template
curve as shown. A perfect curved bevel is the
result.

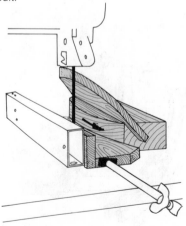

Circles, Discs and Rings

Circular cuts can be made for table tops or stools using the circle cutting attachment. Complete instructions for its use are found in a bandsaw owners manual.

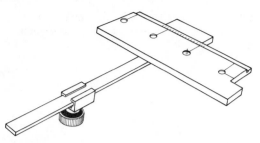

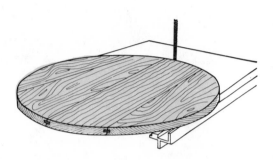

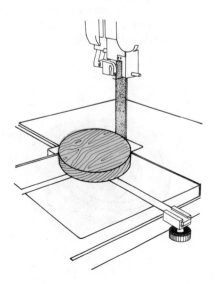

The circle cutting attachment can also be used with the sanding attachment to sand the edges of the discs.

By tilting the bandsaw table, you can use the circle cutting attachment to make cone shaped discs.

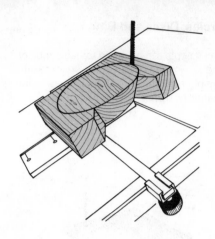

Cutting Rings

By making two cuts for different diameter circles, you can make rings. You will, of course, have to glue the ring together at the point where the blade penetrated it to cut the smaller circle. A thin piece of wood, the same thickness as the saw cut, should be inserted in this cut before gluing.

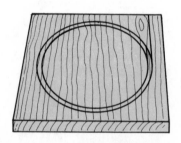

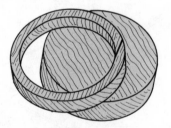

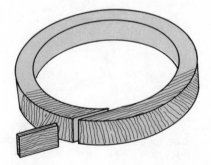

Cutting Contoured Pieces

For Identical Patterns on Both Sides

If the pattern on both sides of a piece is the same, as it is for this chair leg, you only need to make one template. The template should be made of thin plywood, hardboard, or plastic.

Using the template as a guide, mark the cutting lines on both sides of your workpiece.

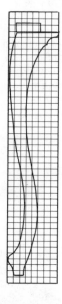

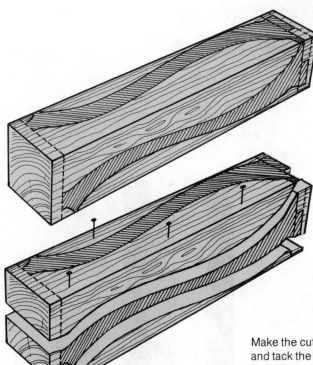

Make the cuts for one side. Stop the machine and tack the wastepieces back in place. Now, turn the piece on its side and make the other cuts. Remove all the wastepieces and your leg, except for sanding, is finished.

For Two Different Patterns

Sometimes, you will find that a furniture part
has two different patterns, or outlines, on each
side. To do this kind of work you will have to
make two different templates, one for each side.
Otherwise, you will follow the same
procedure outlined on the previous page.

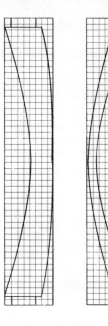

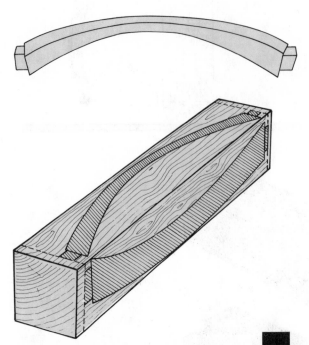

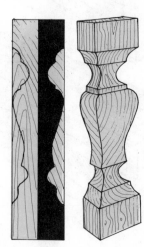

Using a Half Template

A half template was used for this decorative
column, because its design is exactly the same
on all sides. The half template is just flipped
over to layout each side. As before, of course,
the waste of the first cuts is tacked back in place to
make the final cuts.

The Sanding Attachment

By replacing the normal blade with a sanding belt and with the sanding attachment installed, you can sand curved or straight edges. The circle cutting attachment and the mitre guide can be used to support work while sanding.

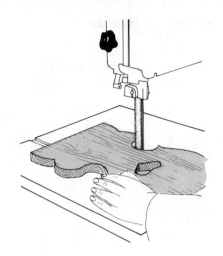

For Inside Curves

Use the curved side of the sanding attachment to sand inside curves. Feed slowly, with light pressure to avoid "digging in".

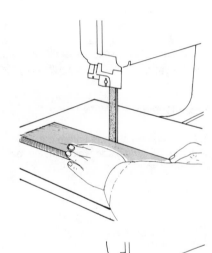

For outside curves and straight surfaces use the flat side of the sanding attachment.

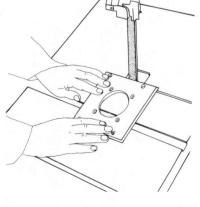

Sanding Steel and Metal

The edges of steel and other metals can be sanded to remove burrs. Before you sand metal, be sure to clean all the wood dust from the inside of the bandsaw. The sparks created while sanding metal could ignite the sawdust.

Sawing Other Materials

Non-ferrous Metals – Aluminium, Brass and Copper

There are special blades made to cut nonferrous metals, which have a smaller set to their teeth and a different tooth pattern. The cutting speed should be reduced, and the feed should be slow.

Plastics

There is no hard and fast rule for sawing plastics. Each different type has its own character. Most hard plastics are brittle and tend to shatter and should be cut with a fine tooth blade. Softer plastics may tend to melt and gum up the spaces between the teeth. For these, a coarse blade should be used with a slow feed.

Foam Materials

These materials are most often cut very well with a knife-band blade which has no teeth, but a very sharp edge.

The Shaper

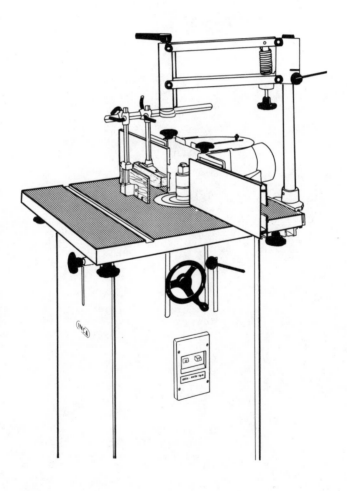

The Cutting Tools

With the correct cutter, you can use your shaper for grooving, making tenons, rabbetting and of course, making decorative moulding. It's very important that you only buy the highest quality cutterheads and cutters for your shaper and use them at, or below, the recommended speed marked on the cutterhead.

Do not use any cutters or cutterheads that have cracks, or that have changed shape in use, or that show any other signs of damage. Make sure that all bolts, screws or nuts that are used to adjust or fasten the cutters are securely tightened before using the machine.

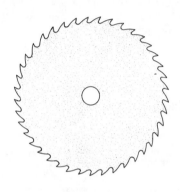

Circular Saw Blades

Rabbets or slits can be cut with a standard circular saw blade. The diameter should be less than 6¼". Use the speed recommended by the blade manufacturer.

Adjustable Grooving Blade

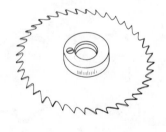

This is a cutting tool that works on the "wobble washer" principle, with the wobble washers built into the hub. Use the scale on the hub to set the width of the groove before mounting the cutter, and be sure that the speed of the machine is set for 6000 rpm. The teeth are ground for cutting with the grain as for grooves and tenons.

The Solid Groover

This is a groover that is made in individual widths, so you must buy the width groovers you need. By using two or more of these cutters with spacers in beween, you can cut tenons, glue joints, or finger joints in one pass.

The Carbide Adjustable Groover

By inserting or removing circular shims, this two piece cutter can be adjusted in width. It is mostly used for shallow grooving, as for drawer sides or cabinet backs.

The Universal Cutter Head

A variety of different replaceable cutters are mounted on this cutterhead in pairs. Also, the angle of the cutters is adjustable. This provides more flexibility in designing new mouldings.

The Cutters

A wide variety of cutters are available to fit the universal cutter head. As you can see, many of these cutters can be used to make several different cuts, and of course you could make several passes with different cutters to make more complex mouldings.

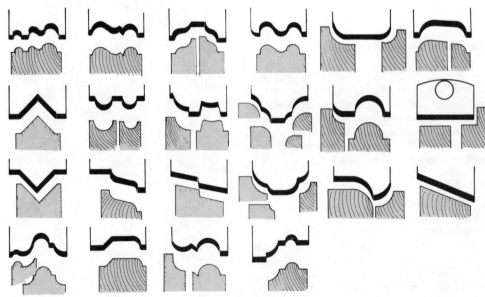

The Universal Cutter Head with Scoring Blades

Four scoring blades mounted in this special universal cutterhead help to prevent tear out and are particularly useful when working on veneered or plastic coated panels.

The Safety Cutter Head

A safety protector bar mounted across from each knife prevents over feeding and kickback by limiting the depth of each cut.

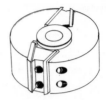

The Replaceable Blade Groover

This groover has scoring blades and cutters that can be rotated in their special holders as they wear and become dull.

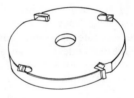

Distance Rings

Distance rings are used above or below the cutter to help position the cutter at the correct height and to allow it to be securely tightened onto the spindle.

Solid Cutters

One piece cutters are also available which have solid steel bodies and carbide knives permanently brazed in place. These are more costly than a replaceable cutter system, but they are always ready to use, and involve no more set-up than mounting them on your machine.

Adjusting the Shaper

The individual cutters should be placed in the cutterhead and adjusted with a moulding head cutter adjuster as shown on p. 16.

An adjusting ruler can be made up from a wooden ruler and a piece of scrap wood. This simple gauge will make the adjustment of your shaper much faster and easier.

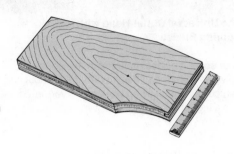

Adjusting the Cutting Depth

Place the adjusting ruler along the fence to measure the cutting depth. To change the depth, move the entire fence and blade cover together. Some models feature a fence on which each fence half can be independently adjusted in and out to control depth of cut.

Adjusting the Cutting Height

Place the edge of the adjusting ruler against the table top and raise or lower the spindle with the handwheel on the side of the machine. Release the spindle lock before turning the handwheel, and re-tighten it after making your adjustment.

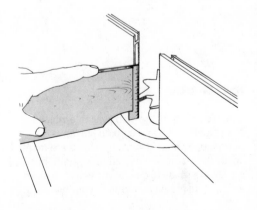

The Safety Hold-down Unit

The safety hold-down unit can be mounted on any side of the table. This provides a great deal of flexibility in making set-ups. It has two pressure feet to hold the work down and in against the fence, and a large spring and parallel arm arrangement to adjust the tension. Because it is easy to use and holds a variety of safety devices, it should be used for all cuts, even trial cuts.

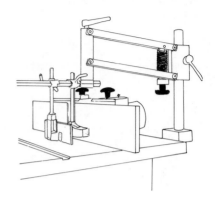

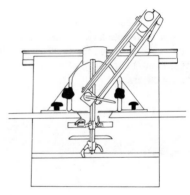

The hold-down unit seen from above.

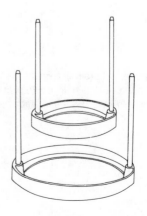

Pressure Shoes and Ring Guards

A variety of different shaped pressure shoes are available to be used with all kinds of work. No work should be done on a shaper without guards and hold-downs.

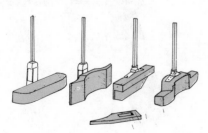

Using the Safety Hold-down-Unit

Shaping the edge of a straight board is the
easiest set-up. The pressure feet are adjusted
to firmly hold the board in place as it is cut.

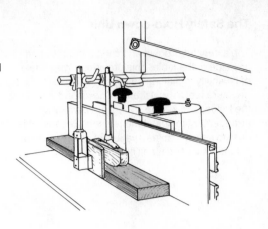

When you work with a very small piece, use the
pressure feet designed for small or narrow
pieces. They are specially shaped to hold small
pieces securely.

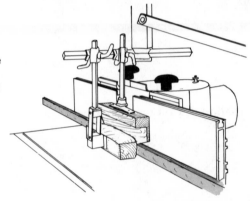

To mould the end grain of a board, use the mitre
guide with the vertical hold-down pressure foot.
The other hold-in foot is left in place as a safety
cover.

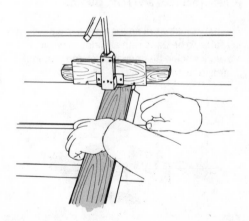

Another way to make this cut is with a large push stick. This pusher will ride along the fence and be cut with the board you are cutting.

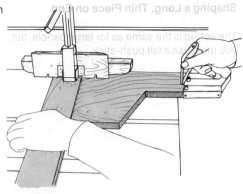

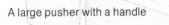

A large pusher with a handle

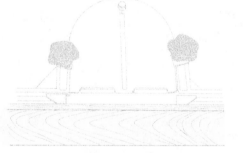

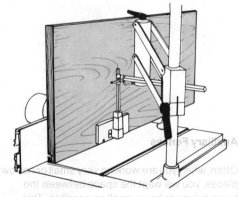

Shaping the Face of a Large Panel

To make cuts of this type, you will move the hold down unit to the front of the machine, facing the fence. The horizontal hold-in pressure foot will press the panel to the fence. The weight of the work and your hand pressure will hold it down. Since the hold down unit is mounted opposite the fence, there will be no height limitation on the work you can shape.

129

Shaping a Long, Thin Piece on End

The set-up is the same as for large panels, but you must use a tall push-stick.

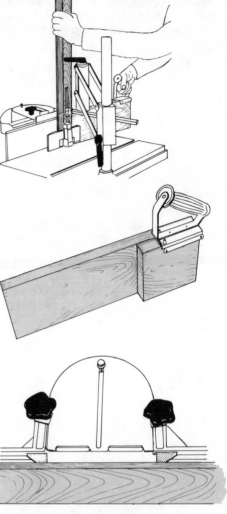

Another push-stick wiht a handle

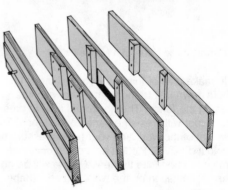

Auxiliary Fences

Often, when you are working very small or narrow pieces, you will want the space between the fence halves to be as small as possible. This is to prevent any pieces from jamming between the cutterhead and fence causing an accident. A variety of fences can be made in the shop quickly out of scrap wood. You can attach them by providing two dovetail shaped ledges to catch the inner ends of the sliding fence parts, or you can install them in place of the metal fences, fastening them in place with two bolts.

Shaping Small Pieces

When working with small pieces, you should use an auxiliary fence with the smallest opening possible and with a steel strip screwed to the bottom edge across the opening. Use the vertical hold-down pressure foot to hold the piece down well and push sticks to hold the pieces in. Then push them through the cutter.

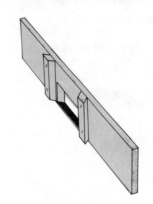

Another push-stick with a handle. This one is used to manipulate small pieces.

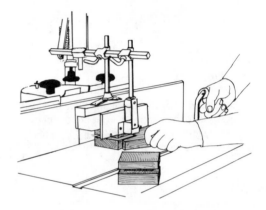

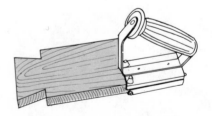

Table Extensions

Under the four sides of the shaper table are dovetail ways and locks made to support extension rails and extension tables. By increasing the size of your work surface, you will make it easier to work long boards.

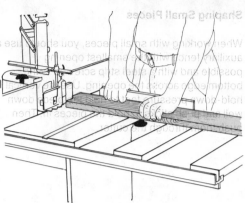

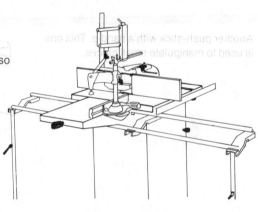

The Sliding Table

As described on p. 45, the sliding table can also be attached to the shaper. It is an important accessory for panel work and for any kind of quantity production.

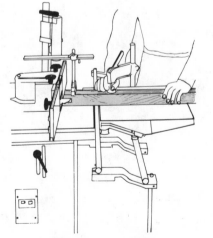

Set-in Cuts

Some straight edge shaping operations must be stopped or started short of one end of the board. Unless this is done properly, it can be very dangerous.

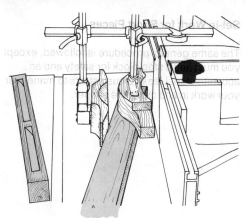

The horizontal hold-in foot must be lowered right to the table. If will not be used to hold in, but as a safety guard.

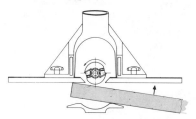

To commence this cut, place the end of the board against the outfeed fence and push the free end against the infeed fence.
Hold the board firmly against the table and fence and complete the cut as usual. Never pull the board back in the direction of the cutter rotation.

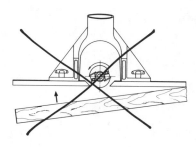

This is the wrong way to start this cut. An accident will surely result.

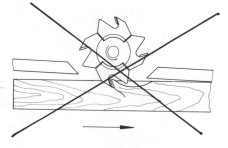

Here is what will happen when the cutter reaches a board that was fed incorrectly. According to government and industry safety boards, most accidents on wood shapers happen because the work was inserted the wrong way.

Set-in Work for Short Pieces

The same general procedure is followed, except you must add a stop block for safety and an accurate start. Use two push sticks to maneuver your work in and out of the shaper.

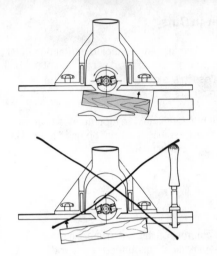

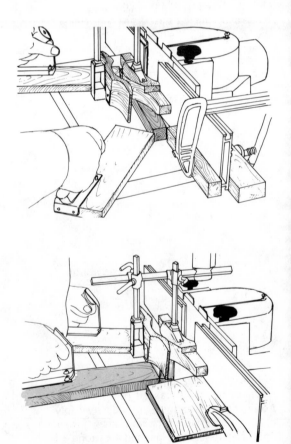

Shaping Contoured Pieces

Using the Ring Guard

The ring guard can be used as a guide surface for patterns which are tacked or screwed to the top of your workpiece. The ring guard should be set at the total height of the workpiece and pattern. The guard should be secured by a ring guard hold-down clamp. A hold-down foot should be positioned over the workpiece to hold it down to the table.

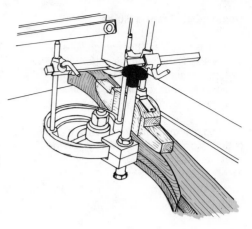

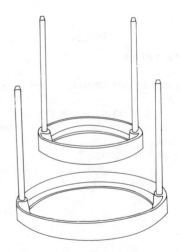

The ring guard hold-down clamp is screwed into the table and clamps the ring guard in place.

Using a Ball Bearing Guide

In this method, a ball bearing guide is mounted on the spindle beneath the cutterhead. The pattern is mounted on the bottom of the workpiece. When the pattern is held against the bearing the cutterhead will cut according to the pattern.

The ring guard should be above and around the cutterhead and set to press down on the workpiece as it is cut.

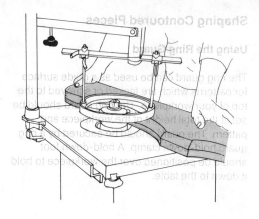

The ball bearing guide

The Infeed Finger

For correct freehand shaping to a pattern, you should always use an infeed finger. This finger is made out of wood in the shape illustrated. You fasten it to the table using the ring guard hold down clamp.

The purpose of this finger is to prevent kickback by allowing you to gradually feed the first part of the work into the revolving cutterhead.

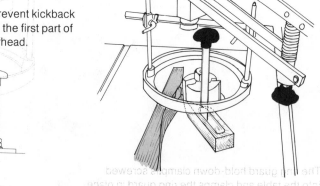

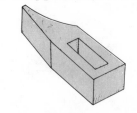

Using the Jointer / Thickness Planer

To do high quality joinery and woodworking, you must properly prepare your stock before layout and cutting. Surfaces must be truly flat and others square and straight.

Lumber fresh from the mill usually warps or twists to some extent as it dries. Even if it does not, the surfaces are generally fairly rough and not completely flat because a lumber mill uses a coarse, fast cutting saw.

To remove this roughness and to establish a sharp, flat surface, the jointer/planer is used. The top of this machine is the jointer. It has two tables, infeed and outfeed, one on each side of a revolving cutterhead. The infeed table is adjustable. To make a cut, the infeed table is lowered, and the board is passed over the cutterhead feeding from the infeed table to the outfeed table.

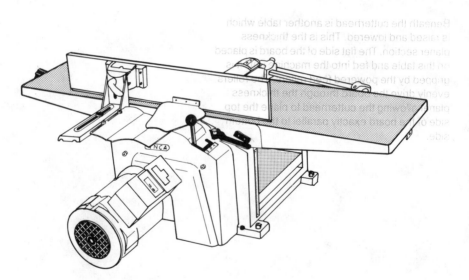

Preparation

To do high quality joinery and woodworking, you must properly prepare your stock before layout and cutting. Surfaces must be truly flat and edges square and straight.

Lumber, fresh from the mill, usually warps or twists to some extent as it dries. Even if it does not, the surfaces are generally fairly rough and not completely flat because a lumber mill uses a coarse, fast cutting saw.

To remove this roughness and to establish a straight, flat surface, the jointer/planer is used. The top of this machine is the jointer. It has two tables, infeed and outfeed, one on each side of a revolving cutterhead. The infeed table is adjustable. To make a cut, the infeed table is lowered, and the board is passed over the cutterhead feeding from the infeed table to the outfeed table.

Beneath the cutterhead is another table which is raised and lowered. This is the thickness planer section. The flat side of the board is placed on this table and fed into the machine until it is gripped by the powered feed rollers. The rollers evenly drive the board through the thickness planer allowing the cutterhead to plane the top side of the board exactly parallel to the bottom side.

The Cutters

Two type of cutters are available: high speed steel and carbide tipped. High speed steel cutters will produce a very fine cut in common woods. They will last between 40 and 120 hours in normal use. Carbide tipped blades are only recommended for cutting plywood, chipboard, plastics, and highly abrasive tropical woods. Because of the high cost of carbide knives, it is often more sensible to buy two sets of high speed steel cutters instead of one set of carbide tipped ones. When using carbide knives, you must be very careful. Although carbide will hold an edge for a long time, it is a brittle material and will not withstand rough handling without chipping.

The Cutterhead

The cutterhead is made of one piece of solid steel with grooves cut into it to hold the cutters and their backing plates. Each cutter has a specially shaped steel backing plate which is held securely against the cutter by a series of locking screws. Beneath each end of each cutter is a special adjusting screw used to raise and lower the cutter. The cutters must be carefully adjusted to get the smoothest possible planed surface.

A new design cutterhead is now available in many parts of the world. This cutterhead uses a special cutter that slides in through the side of the cutterhead. To release this cutter, tap the backing plate behind it and slide the old cutters out, and the slide the new cutters in. Because of its unique design, this cutterhead does not need or use locking or adjusting screws to hold the blade in place. The blade and backing plate are completely captive, and lock firmly in place as soon as the machine in switched on. And, you can change the cutters in this new cutterhead in a matter of seconds.

Safety notes

- Always change both cutters at the same time.
- Loosen the locking screws slightly before raising or lower the cutters.
- Always check the locking screws for tightness before you use the machine.
- Check cutters for cracks. Discard cracked cutters as they are dangerous.

Surface or Face Planing

You will always start working a fresh board by surface planing one side to establish a flat and straight reference surface.

The guards should always be used, covering the cutters at all times.

To surface plane a board, you will cut the concave, or cupped, side first. This is to minimize any tendency of the board to "rock" from side to side as it is cut.

Hold the concave side of the board down against the infeed table with firm, controlled pressure.

Slowly slide the board with your right hand until the cutterhead begins to cut. After about 10" have been cut, press down on the board, over the outfeed table, with your left hand and continue sliding the board until the cut is complete. Be careful not to feed too fast or to rock the board as you make this cut. Always keep your hands on top of the board and never allow your fingers to come near the cutterhead. Do not press the board down over the cutterhead. Push sticks should be used for small or short pieces.

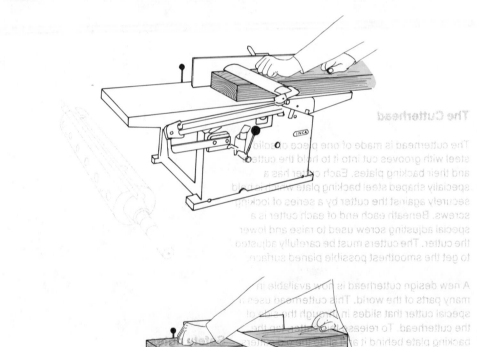

Edge Jointing

With one surface planed flat and straight you will now joint one edge straight and square to the flat surface.

Lower the guard to the table and pull the end back until the board can just pass between the end of the guard and the fence.

Hold the flat side of the board against the fence and slide the edge of the board over the cutterhead from the infeed table to the outfeed table, as in surface planing.

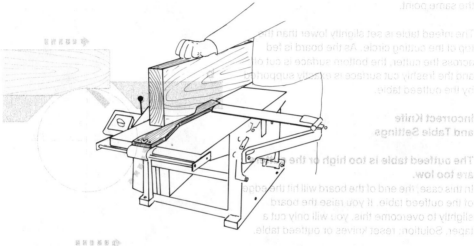

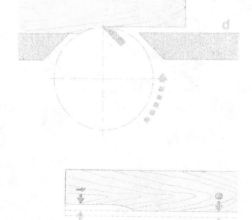

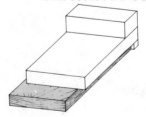

Table and Cutter Position

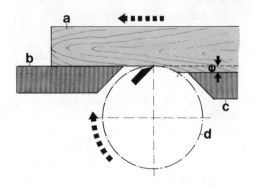

a. Board being cut.
b. Outfeed table.
c. Infeed table.
d. Cutting circle of the rotating cutters.
e. Depth of cut.
Boards should always be jointed or planed with the grain (as shown) for the smoothest surface finish.

The jointer consists of an infeed table "c", and an outfeed table "b". The outfeed table surface and the top of the cutting circle "d" must be at the same point.

The infeed table is set slightly lower than the top of the cutting circle. As the board is fed across the cutter, the bottom surface is cut off and the freshly cut surface is exactly supported by the outfeed table.

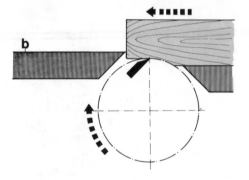

Incorrect Knife and Table Settings

The outfeed table is too high or the cutters are too low.
In this case, the end of the board will hit the edge of the outfeed table. If you raise the board slightly to overcome this, you will only cut a taper. Solution: reset knives or outfeed table.

The outfeed table is too low or the cutters are too high.
The symptom of this condition is a "snipe" at the end of the board as shown below. Solution: reset the knives or the outfeed table.

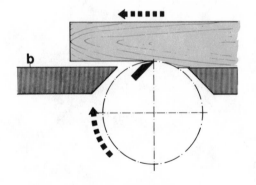

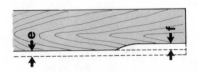

The Jointer Fence

The angle of the fence should be checked and adjusted by using a high quality try square, or a block of dry hardwood cut to the required angle.

You should move the fence to different positions over the cutterhead from time to time to help insure even cutter wear.

The rear cutter guard should always completely cover the cutterhead beneath it.

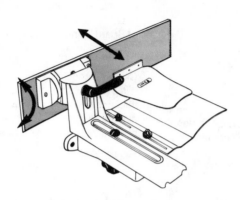

The Jointer Guard

This type of guard can be raised, lowered, and positioned in or out for jointing or surface planing. Always use the guard positioned as close to the work, fence and cutterhead as possible.

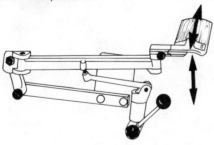

Thickness Planing

Thickness planing makes one side of your board absolutely parallel to the other and, of course, of even thickness.

First, one side of the board must be absolutely flat. A board can only be accurately thickness planed when one side has been first surfaced planed on the jointer.

The flat side of the board is placed against the thicknessing table "f" and fed beneath the limit rod "a". The board must pass easily below this rod. Use the height adjustment crank to raise or lower the table. Then the board passes beneath the anti-kickback fingers "b", is pulled in by the infeed roller "c" beneath the cutterhead "d", and on to the outfeed roller (not shown) which pulls the board the rest of the way through the machine.

Parts of the Thickness Planer
a) Limit rod
b) Anti-kickback fingers
c) Powered infeed roller
d) Cutterhead
e) Board being planed
f) Thickness table

Cleaning and Polishing
It is a good idea to clean and polish the thicknessing table often with a suitable wax/cleaner (eg INCA Waxilit), expecially if you are planing very wet or resinous board.

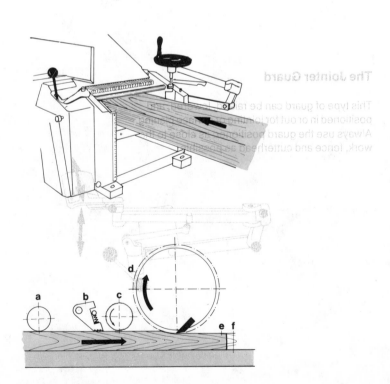

Thickness Planer Feed Speeds

Use the higher speed (2) for softwoods and rough cutting. Use the lower speed (1) for the last finish cuts and for hardwoods.

If the board jams while planing
1. Lower the thicknessing bed. Sometimes one section of a rough board will be much thicker than another. In this case, you must set your depth of cut for the thickest part of the board and work down in a series of passes.
2. Polish and wax the bed.
3. Check the drive belt tension as described in your owners manual or consult with your dealer.

Planing Thin Stock

To plane very thin boards you will have to use an auxiliary wooden table on top of the thickness planer table.

Using this auxiliary table, feed your boards through at slow speed and use a light cut. You will be able to plane thinner than $1/16$" with most woods. Thin strips can be used to make woven fences as illustrated.

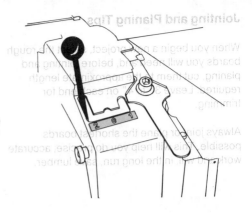

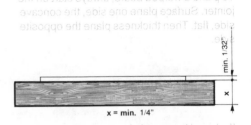

x = min. 1/4"

Jointing and Planing Tips

When you begin a new project, select the rough boards you will need and, before jointing and planing, cut them to the approximate length required. Leave 3" to 4" on each end for trimming.

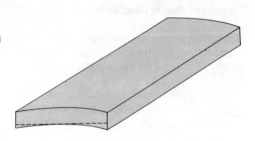

Always joint or plane the shortest boards possible. This will help you do precise, accurate work and will, in the long run, save lumber.

To plane a warped board, always start on the jointer. Surface plane one side, the concave side, flat. Then thickness plane the opposite side.

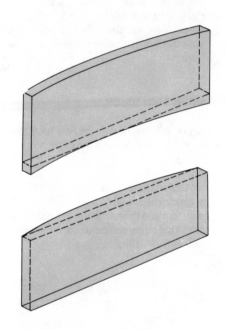

If a board is warped along one edge, surface plane one side first. Then joint the concave edge straight, holding the flat planed surface against the fence. The other edge can be made parallel to the first by feeding the board through the thickness planer on edge, if it is not too wide, or by using a table saw or bandsaw and its rip fence.

A twisted board is tricky to plane accurately. A little practice is necessary. First mark the high point on one side. Then, carefully controlling the board by hand, surface plane the high points off until the board is stable and will not rock when cut. Proceed as normally. If at all possible, cut long twisted boards down to shorter lengths.

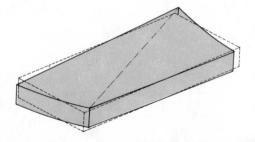

This is a section cut through a warped piece of lumber. To make this piece perfectly square, first surface plane one side. Then hold that side against the fence and joint the adjoining side. Finally, feed the board through the thickness planer with the planed sides placed down against the thickness table.

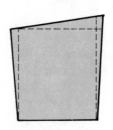

When thickness planing be sure that the workpiece is held flat on the thickness table as it is fed in and removed from the machine. For long boards, use of an outfeed roller or stand is wise.

This is a section cut through a warped piece of lumber. To make this piece perfectly square, first surface plane one side. Then hold that side against the fence and joint the adjoining side. Finally, feed the board through the thickness planer with the planed sides placed down against the thickness table.

When thickness planing be sure that the workpiece is held flat on the thickness table as it is fed in and removed from the machine. For long boards, use of an outfeed roller or stand is wise.

Wood –
an Organic Material

Structure, Shrinkage and Glueing

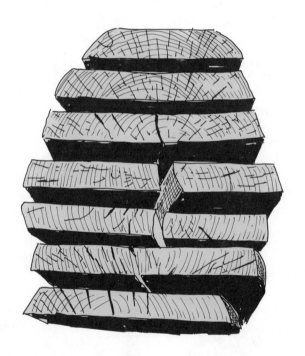

Cross Section of a Tree

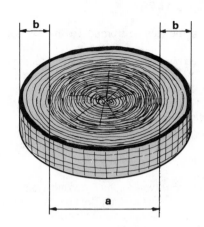

Cut straight across, a tree trunk shows a series of concentric growth rings with its bark on the outside and a pith at the center. The pith is very small, and is actually the remains of the original shoot or stem. In older, mature trees, the pith is often dried out and forms the "pith tube" in the center of the tree.

Around the pith or pith tube is the heartwood (section "a"), which forms the largest part of the trunk. Surrounding the heartwood is the sapwood. The sapwood carries water and nutrients through the tree. It is also where the growth of the trunk takes place. Each year the sapwood ring closest to the center of the tree becomes heartwood and a new ring of sapwood is grown.

The Appearance of the Board's Surface

Because wood is a growing, organic material, each board will have a unique appearance. This depends both on the kind of wood and how the board was cut from the log. By selecting boards carefully, you can create a variety of decorative effects.

Section "a" shows the tree cut across, exposing the annual growth rings and the "end grain". At section "b", the tree is cut "radially" that is in a straight line from pith to outside edge. This type of cut slices through each annual ring and also exposes the "medullary" rays. These are special cells that grow between the rings from the pith to the bark in many species. Wood cut this way often shows a "silvery" or "silky" surface, and is sometimes referred to as "mirror cut". Cutting the tree at a tangent to the growth rings, as in section "c" exposes a variety of different cell structures which will often absorb stains and finishes at different rates.

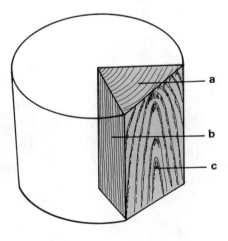

Few trees, of course, grow in perfect cylinders with each ring exactly concentric to the others. Branches will change the structure where they enter the truck and wind and weather will affect how the tree grows. This is part of the fascination of working with wood, since each piece of board will be a little different from all others.

Ripping a Log

After a tree is cut, it is brought to the mill to be ripped into boards. How the log is cut is often dictated by what is most economical for the mill – the method that will create the largest amount of usable lumber from a particular log. As a woodworker you should learn to "read" the growth rings on the end of a board as well as the pattern of the faces. This will help tell you how the boards you buy may warp and twist as they dry.

The cheapest way for the mill to cut a log is shown in illustration "a". The boards in the center will shrink evenly and be reasonably free from warp or twist. The ones to the left and right of center will warp – the ones closest to the outside the most. All these boards will have

bark on their edges, and the edges will not be square.

The same type of cut is made in illustration "b", but the log is squared first, so that the edges of most of the boards are reasonably straight and square.

Illustrations "c" and "d" show other cutting patterns that will yield a larger number of boards relatively free from warp.

Finally illustration "e" shows a log that has been "quarter-sawn". Nearly every board taken from this log will remain straight and free from warp.

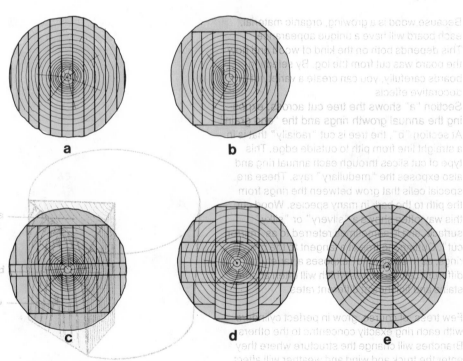

a

b

c

d

e

Wood Movement

As a freshly cut board dries, the moisture in the wood fibres evaporates and the board shrinks. This will continue until the moisture in the wood and the humidity in the air reach a point of equilibrium. After that, the board will shrink or expand slightly as the humidity in the air changes.

A board will shrink or expand more in some directions than in others. As a rough guide:
a) Along the length of the board: 1/10%
b) Along the radius of the tree: 5%
c) Along a tangent to the growth rings: 10%

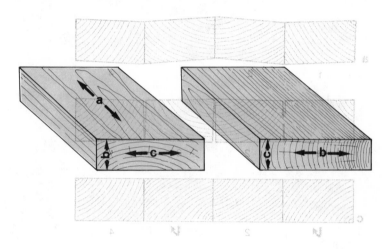

As an example, this section of a board was square when it was just cut. After drying, it is no longer square. As you can imagine, this effect can be very important when you glue a series of boards together.

153

Gluing Boards Togehter

Glue joints are strongest when the long grain of the first board is glued parallel to the long grain of the second. Second best is when the grain of two boards cross each other at right angles. End grain glued to long grain makes the weakest joint. When two boards must be joined end grain to long grain as in a frame, box or corner joint, a mortise and tenon, dowel or finger joint is used. Not only it is this physically stronger, the long grain will be crossed at right angles and will make a very strong glue joint. The correct way to glue a series of boards together into a panel is to turn every other board face down. Illustrations "a" and "b" show panels glued together with the inside of each board facing up. The result is a "wavy" surface. A panel that is correctly glued is shown in illustration "c".

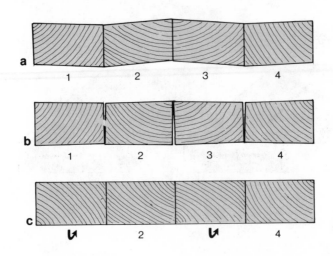

Boards cut from the tree on a radius have less tendency to warp than those cut on a tangent. For example, the top illustration shows a board cut from the center of the tree. It will shrink straight and evenly. The next two illustrations show boards cut off-center. These two will warp because the largest amount of shrinkage is around the circumference of the growth rings and also because of the uneven distribution of heartwood and sapwood. Boards with long complete growth rings will generally warp quite a bit, as shown in the bottom illustration.

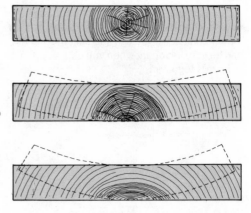

When you must glue two boards together, face to face to make a thicker one, follow these rules: glue the boards together outside to outside as shown; use boards of the same thickness. These two precautions will prevent the glue line from opening at the edges and will reduce excessive tension in the finished product.

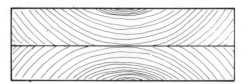

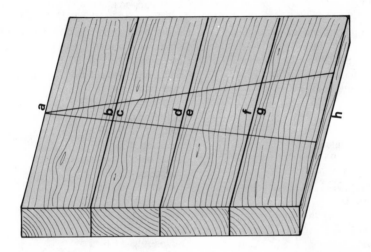

When gluing a series of boards into a panel, lay them out dry first and draw a triangle on the top surface with a pencil or chalk as shown. Then, stack them and brush glue onto the right side edges (d,f,g,b). Using the triangle as a guide, lay them out again and clamp well with bar clamps.

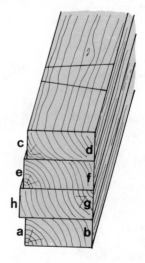

Always clamp glue joints well after assembly and leave undisturbed until the glue sets. Follow the glue manufacturer's, directions.

INDEX